THE WHITE ALLY TOOLKIT WORKBOOK

USING ACTIVE LISTENING, EMPATHY, AND PERSONAL STORYTELLING TO PROMOTE RACIAL EQUITY

Heather, Thanks for your allyship!
David Campt
11-16-19

FIRST EDITION

BY DAVID W. CAMPT, PHD

I AM Publications

The White Ally Toolkit Workbook: Using Active Listening, Empathy, and Personal Storytelling to Promote Racial Equity

I AM Publications

(617) 564-1060

contact@iampubs.com

www.iampubs.com

Printed in the United States of America

First Edition, 2018

ISBN: 978-1-943382-03-3

IN APPRECIATION

Anyone on a journey through difficulties needs allies. It is important to pause to directly express thanks for the special kind of support that many folks have given so this workbook could come to be:

To Mike Novogratz and Katie Weitz, for giving the resourceful guidance that forward thinking philanthropists can;

To Lucky Lynch, Paige Eaves, Judith Mowry, Sybil Madison, and Ivan Cutler, for picking up the phone now and then and being the cheerleaders vitally needed so that a vague and fuzzy vision could become something concrete;

To Mike Barney, Monica Butler, Lisa Thompson, and Beth Castle for the reminders of the value of emotional support;

To Theo Brown and McCrae Parker, for being willing to talk about the intricacies of dialogue repeatedly and well into the early morning;

To Ngozi Robinson and Matthew Freeman, who each exquisitely combine the central roles of thought partners and "do" partners;

To caregivers Steven Neal, Mary Chatman, Margaret Stewart, and Willie Walker, whose teamwork in allyship in parental caregiving was essential in creating a year with the least number of nights in the hospital as any in the past half-decade;

To Vietta and Arnai Johnson, whose perseverance through trials is one of many reminders of the need of discipline, focus, and the never ending need for keeping an calm eye on the prize;

To James and Geraldine Campt, whose amazing positivity still fuels, and whose lessons about the importance of good communication have driven my lifelong passion for dialogue;

To Stephanie Ballard, for piloting the workshop with White People for Racial Justice of San Gabriel Valley, and for careful copy-editing of this workbook;

And finally, to all who serve humanity by actively spending their precious human energy on causes bigger than their own.

TABLE OF CONTENTS

Don't be in such a hurry to condemn a person because he doesn't do what you do, or think as you think or as fast. There was a time when you didn't know what you know today.

– Malcolm X

PURPOSE OF THIS WORKBOOK

For too long, the call for an "honest dialogue about race" has been thought about as a conversation between white folks and people of color (POC). As important as that conversation is, the idea behind this workbook is that some progress on race relations is best achieved through conversation among white people. According to public opinion polls in 2017, about 55% of white people think that racism against white people is as big of a societal problem as racism against POC. Unless white public opinion is shifted, it will be difficult to create initiatives that address the significant problems related to racial equity.

This workbook springs from the Ally Conversation Toolkit, or ACT, with a goal to flip this 45/55 split by 2025. For this to occur, many things are needed, such as better articulation about racism from diverse political and corporate leaders, better messaging about race in mass and social media, and more sophisticated talk about race in our education systems. What is also needed is effective one-on-one conversation between white people who know that racism is a special burden on POC and those who think that racism affects every group equally.

It would be neither fair nor feasible for POC to carry the burden of having these conversations. There are not enough POC - or conversely, there are too many white folks – for that to work. And POC are increasingly fatigued by educating white people; they are already dealing with the additional burden of actually coping with racism. Of course, some of that educational work by POC is much needed; open-minded white folks need to hear the stories about what racism looks like in modern day America. It is time to shift the burden of educating racism-denying white folks away from POC, and onto those who might be considered white comrades in the fight against racism.

This workbook and the ACT project is based on the idea that allies who resist societal oppression (isms such as racism, sexism, or homophobia) need to create community in a very mindful way in order to have effective conversations with others who are also not direct targets of that ism.

(To clarify, when the "ism" in question is racism, the work of the Ally Conversation Toolkit is referred to as the White Ally Toolkit.) These white folks need to prepare for these conversations by doing some reflective work of their own – by themselves, in groups with other like-minded white people, and preferably both.
This workbook addition, helps with white people anti-POC racism matters also need to have a strategy designed racism denial. To put it directly, white people who care about addressing racism need to learn a version what people of color have been doing for centuries, which is code switching. This term refers to a practice of speaking differently in different settings in order to increase one's effectiveness. Discussing racism with those who are not like-minded needs to be done very differently than with those who have a shared understanding that racism exists. This workbook is designed to foster the deep, reflective, internal work that is needed, to describe a strategy for this code switching, and to give guidance about how to apply it in a variety of situations.

> Too many white folks readily talk about "checking their privilege" to their POC friends and other whites who are "woke" without having the long, slow, frustrating, and socially risky series of conversations with their Cousin Hannah or Uncle Tristan (to use a couple of white names) who don't think racism against people of color is real.

White allies need to be much more serious about the work of having effective conversations with people who deny racism. In the view of this project, it is not enough to go to white ally meetings or to work with POC on institutional change. Of course, these are very important activities.

But too many white folks readily talk about "checking their privilege" without having the long, slow, frustrating, and socially risky series of conversations with their Cousin Hannah or Uncle Tristan (to use a couple of white names) who don't think racism against POC is real. Besides taking this obligation seriously, white allies need to more deeply analyze what is working and not working as they try to change the perspective of those in their circle of influence. The goal of this project -- and the website www.allyconversationtoolkit.com – is to help white allies see the task of using their influence to bring other whites along (i.e. "woking" others up) as part of their lifelong mission in dismantling racism. This project also hopes those white allies who are somewhat "wokish" will join together in learning communities dedicated to woking others.

This project's approach to racial equity work is well within the progressive anti-racism tradition. However it is different than that used by many racial equity advocates today. It is useful to lift some of these differences up explicitly.

PROPHETIC VOICE V. DIALOGIC ENGAGEMENT

The core approach of ACT is that white allies should engage people who deny isms, listen to them without judgment, share stories that build trust, and try to expand their sense of how the -ism works through stories, data or useful concepts. As mentioned, this will usually not happen in a single conversation. The research that backs this approach to engagement will be later reviewed.

This empathetic listening approach is in sharp contrast to the way many racial justice advocates approach conversations about race with people who are not on board with their point of view. Partly out of frustration with the slow progress on racism, many racial justice advocates only talk about racial issues in what could be called a "prophetic voice." This approach to discussing racial topics emphasizes unvarnished truth-telling, calling out the hypocrisies of others, sharing a deep analysis of racial power, and confronting people with the hard truth of racism and how it harms POC.

INTRODUCTION

The prophetic voice is a vital part of social change, especially when organizing people. When trying to mobilize people against an opponent, it is important to draw sharp distinctions, to portray opponents as deeply flawed, and to diminish the sense of ambiguities in the situation. Such portrayals – especially in group settings - can be very energizing to existing allies, and sometimes to people who are on the fence.

> When trying to influence people who doubt the reality of racism, it is more effective to listen to them, and to draw out how they feel about race, racism, and issues related to it.

However, this prophetic voice is less helpful in one-on-one and small group conversations. Moreover,the prophetic voice is not just unproductive when talking to people who disagree with you, it is often counterproductive.

This project is based on helping people who think anti-POC racism matters to cultivate a set of communication strategies that are more akin to a coach guiding a novice player than a prophet speaking to a congregation. When coaching, it is important to demonstrate patience and empathy, and to purposefully choose topics and strategies that are adapted to the moment. When trying to influence people who doubt the reality of racism, it is more effective to listen and to draw out how they feel about race, racism, and issues related to it. (See the section in Part One titled Why White Allies Must Take Over the Work of Woking.) This way of engaging could be described as one that calls upon an ally's skills in dialogic engagement, instead of their ability to capture the prophetic voice.

TERMINOLOGY

Every term involved in social justice work has been deconstructed, analyzed, and almost inevitably found problematic. Some people don't like the term "ally" for a variety of reasons, many of which make sense. For the sake of this discussion about how to move white public opinion, this terminology is not particularly important. The use of the term "white ally" in this workbook is meant as shorthand for any white person who thinks that racism against POC is a special problem, and who sometimes takes specific action to combat it. As noted, this is slightly less than half of adult white Americans.

Similarly, we will use the term racism skeptic to refer to the slightly more than half of white folks who think that racism against POC is no worse that racism against whites, and who don't think that they or society have a special obligation to address this problem.

WHITE FRAGILITY

In the past few years, white fragility has emerged as a concept to explain how some white people become dysfunctional within conversations about race, typically when interacting with one or more people of color.[1] Examples of white fragility are excessive tears, anger, frustration, and questioning well-established facts in a way that tends to derail a conversation. Part of the idea of labeling it is to make two points: 1) it is difficult to keep some white folks engaged in a meaningful race conversation, and 2) their counterproductive emotional reaction is often not primarily a function of the behavior of the POC who are present.

Despite deep misgivings about whether this term is the best way to label this behavior, this project takes white fragility very seriously. Arguably, the core motivation for this project is to make large-scale progress on racial attitudes, while not putting the burden on POC to navigate the behavior. The expectation is that white folks will be noticeably less fragile when they

---

1 This term was coined by Robin DiAngelo, The International Journal of Critical Pedegogy, Vol. 3, Number 3, 2011.

are talking about race with another white person, and when they are not in a large group situation. Even so, this fragility is real, and can be an obstacle to looking racism square in the face.

This project suggests that the best methods for influencing racism skeptics are to take very gradual, non-confrontational approaches to conversation, and to do this in ways that are less likely to activate white fragility. To do that, you should not think of yourself as attempting a quick conversion. Although now and then people have epiphanies after poignant and logically tight sermonettes about racism, allies should not count on this. Racial skepticism has a deep background in America, and has been long brewing in individuals. When it comes to working with skeptics, an ally needs to be always ready, but never in a hurry. This is long and slow work.

POLITICAL IDEOLOGY

For a variety of reasons, many racism skeptics are on the right/conservative side of the political spectrum, and many white allies are on the left/liberal side.[2] Of course, this is not universally true, as there are allies who are conservative and skeptics who are liberal. But realistically, if the white ally population is to reduce the number of skeptics out there, there will have to be lot of conversations between liberals and conservatives. It is worth noting that if people can figure out how to have such conversations successfully, it might have additional benefits outside of the race context.

This project does not take the position that bringing white skeptics out of their racism denial necessarily means getting them to abandon their conservative beliefs. In fact, trying to shift a skeptic's general worldview is much too big a goal, and may undermine your attempt to reduce their denial about racism. Political worldview is deeply ingrained,and people are often extremely attached to their perspective. (Some implications

2 According to a 2017 survey by Pew Research, 75% of Republicans think that blacks who can't get ahead in the US are responsible for their own condition, while 66% of white Democrats said that racial discrimination is the reason that blacks can't get ahead. http://www.people-press.org/2017/10/05/4-race-immigration-and-discrimination/

of political worldviews will be explored in the Odds and Ends section.) This project is not designed to assist with turning conservatives to liberals. If enough liberal allies are successful in bringing conservatives out of racism denial, the conservative movement will have to grapple with how to expand anti-racist discourse within political conservatism. That is a healthy goal that progressive allies should support.

> This project does not take the position that bringing white skeptics out of their denial of racism necessarily means getting them to abandon their conservative beliefs.

ANECDOTES FROM PEOPLE OF COLOR

As the idea of white allies against racism has grown in recent years, the number of support groups has increased, as have the amount of literature. Much of this literature has focused on how white allies and POC can work in healthy partnership toward changing institutions and creating multi-racial settings. Groups such as Showing Up for Racial Justice, Coming to the Table AWARE-LA, the YWCA and others are to be admired for their efforts that result in productive encounters across racial lines. When such cross-racial encounters occur, there are many complexities to manage. Issues of bias, privilege, stereotypes, and structural advantage can remain challenges, even if everyone has the same basic belief that racism matters.

This workbook acknowledges that cross-racial challenges can be difficult, and that allies will benefit from thinking about these topics. However, this workbook will not address the complexity of creating such settings or managing these difficulties.

Nevertheless, there is recognition that white allies will be more effective if they have some reasonable degree of emotionally honest contact with people of color, both as personal friends and as a part of a culturally

> White allies will be more effective if they have some reasonable degree of emotionally honest contact with people of color, both as personal friends and as a part of a culturally diverse group that encourages the discussion of racism.

diverse group that encourages the discussion of racism. Cross-racial friendships will hopefully nurture white allies, as well as provide occasional feedback for their ongoing journey as anti-racists. These friendships are important for an additional reason. Specifically, the conversational approach suggested in this workbook is grounded fundamentally in listening and sharing stories. Every person has a race, so we all have stories about how race has affected us. This applies to white folks too, even if they need to do some introspective digging to unearth them. But it is useful to have stories from POC whom you know personally and with whom you have relationships of mutual trust. At the right time, deploying a secondhand story from a POC you trust may be very effective.

TONE AND PERSPECTIVE

As this project has delivered workshops to boost white ally effectiveness across the country, many people of color have participated. Most have found the material useful in helping understand the dynamics of influencing people we disagree with. Similarly, people of color are welcomed to spend time with this workbook.

Even though the basis of the tools offered in this workbook is findings from social psychology and cognitive studies and persuasion science that are applicable to everyone, the tools themselves are specifically aimed at white anti-racism allies. Accordingly, the tone will sometimes speak to the reader as "you," with the presumption is that the reader is a white person.

The expectation is that this workbook will be used primarily by individuals, but some white ally groups may make influencing racism skeptics an important part of their collective work. In several places, we will provide additional guidance for processes that groups can use to deepen people's understanding of the material. As this project goes forward, it will produce a Discussion Leaders' Guide that will be useful for people wanting to guide a group through a multi-session program to deeply integrate the content into their personal ally practice.

USING THIS WORKBOOK

This workbook is primarily a set of worksheets designed to help you prepare for encounters with racism skeptics. Sprinkled among the worksheets are guidance and explanations of the thinking behind the worksheets, essays, and commentary, references to research materials, and a few lists that may be useful. The workbook is arranged in four parts, each with a number of separate elements briefly described here.

1 PART ONE:

KNOWING YOURSELF

Part One helps white allies gain more discernment as they take a detailed look at several aspects of the history and current practice of interacting with racism skeptics.

Ally PRIORITIES Ranking Tool

This tool helps white allies take an honest look at areas of allyship they are focusing on, balancing effort spent and results gained. The tool covers a number of dimensions of white allyship, even though the rest of the workbook only focuses on the specific dimension of working with racism skeptics. This section is particularly useful if you are not clear that you want to spend a greater proportion your ally energy on engaging skeptics.

Why white allies must take over THE WORK OF "WOKING"

This subsection reviews different lines of argument about why white allies should increase their energy toward changing other white folks' minds, and why they should engage their peers very differently than they often do now. This section is particularly useful if you need to be reminded of reasons why white allies should spend more time engaging skeptics and why it is important for them to do so by in a manner that emphasizes empathic listening.

Ally Listening SELF-ASSESSMENT Tools

This interactive instrument is a set of four worksheets augmented by commentary that encourages you to look clearly at your listening patterns. In addition, some listening tips that other white allies have found helpful are provided. This section is particularly useful if you are not sure that your listening skills are maximally effective.

Creating Your LISTENING Best Practices Tool

This subsection reviews some best practices in listening and encourages you to create a best practice list personalized to you. Knowing your own best practices will be useful when you get frustrated with racism skeptics.

The White Ally RESPONSE Assessment Tool

This tool helps allies notice what they do when people say or do racially-problematic things in their presence. It turns out there are some common patterns. This section is particularly useful if you have not done much thinking about how you tend to respond in these situations.

PART TWO:

USING THE RACE METHOD TO ENGAGE RACISM DENIAL

Part Two focuses on preparing you to address racially-problematic statements that emerge from time to time.

The RACE Method – An Overview

This subsection explains the core strategy of dialogic engagement that the White Ally Toolkit advocates. It explains the general method that will reappear and be adapted to specific racism-denying statements in the modules sections.

STRUCTURE of the Modules

This reviews how the modules are presented and offers guidelines about when different aspects of the modules will be helpful to you.

Combating Racism Denial - THE MODULES

These short pieces provide detailed guidance of how white allies can use the RACE Method to turn racially-problematic statements into opportunities for dialogue and learning. There are eight modules, each based on specific racism-denying statements that skeptics often make. Over time, more modules will be created and will appear on the project website and in future editions of this workbook. The modules are:

1. "Racism means having intentionally negative views of other groups. So if I don't have conscious negative intent, I don't have to worry about being racist."
2. "Nowadays, there are very few advantages to being white. I am not 'privileged".
3. "Very few people are consciously racist anymore."
4. "Slavery and segregation were a long time ago. We should not talk about them anymore and just move on."
5. "The economic problems of people of color are primarily due to the bad choices that they make."
6. "If people of color would just act properly, law enforcement would treat them fairly."
7. "It is vital that America drastically reduce the level of immigration so that we can return to our cultural greatness."
8. "Those athletes protesting should be grateful that they live in America and should not disrespect the nation and the flag by kneeling during the National Anthem."

3 PART THREE:

THE ALLY COACHING CURRICULUM

Part Three prepares allies who want to intentionally focus on a person's racial awareness and strengthen it over time.

THE PRIMER—KEY CONCEPTS OF INTERPERSONAL RACISM

This section is intended to serve as a lesson plan for allies who want to intentionally engage someone in a series of focused conversations. The primer focuses on the key phenomena in race relations that can be directly experienced by individuals, and provides reflection questions to examine your own experiences with some discernment before you ask the skeptic to do so. Each topic provides multiple potential paths you might take in upgrading the skeptic's awareness.

Racial Issues - THE COLLECTIVE CONCEPTS

This essay highlights key concepts about race that are largely collective concepts that cannot as easily be observed through individual experience. To grasp these concepts, it is generally necessary to use statistics, data, and other lenses.

* Othering
* Unconscious bias
* Attribution error
* Racial anxiety
* Unearned racial advantage (commonly called white privilege)
* Racial threat
* Racial Backlash/Denial
* Institutional Racism
* Structural Racism
* Racial Inequity/Equity

4 PART FOUR:
ODDS AND ENDS

Part Four includes instruments and commentary that did not fit within other sections but are useful to allies in increasing their focus on influencing skeptics.

The subsections within Odds and Ends can be summarized in the core questions that they focus on:

- **Past experiences of people trying to influence each other – What has your experience been of different approaches to engaging racism skeptics?**
- **Continuum of retorts – What are some possible things to say when dialogue is not an option?**
- **Shame: Does it affect your work as an ally? – Is unprocessed racial shame affecting you?**
- **Choosing skeptics to engage – How do I make good choices about who to invest energy on?**
- **Creating an informal ally practice group**
- **Creating a formal practice group with a facilitator**
- **Using insights about conservative and liberal moral frameworks – How can I leverage research about worldviews to improve my ally practice?**
- **Why anti-racist progressives need to support conservatives – Is there a role for progressives in creating anti-racist conservatism?**
- **Closing encouragements – What are some key points to remember so I can stay on the path?**

RESOURCES
ADDITIONAL RESOURCES

A listing of resources allies might use to bolster their understanding of some key topics that this workbook has reviewed.

Some resources that allies might use to bolster their understanding of key topics in this workbook.

* Othering
* Unconscious Bias
* Attribution Error
* Racial Anxiety
* Unearned Racial Advantage (Commonly Called White Privilege)
* Racial Threat
* White Backlash
* Institutional Racism Vs Structural Racism
* Racial Inequity

PART ONE: KNOWING YOURSELF

Part One helps white allies gain more discernment as they take a detailed look at several aspects of the history and current practice of interacting with racism skeptics.

As stated, this project emerges from the idea that white allies are not effectively leveraging their influence with racism skeptics. This critique is offered with the understanding that there are many things that a white ally could do with their "ally time" and that they are human beings who have other interests besides racial equity. It would be great if everyone made racial justice the top priority of their life, but it is not likely anytime soon. Allies who have different levels of commitment and focus on racial issues need to be conscious and intentional about which activities will comprise their ally practice,as well as how effective these practices are.

> The white ally community is systematically under-investing in the task of influencing skeptics, and this has very important social, institutional, and political consequences.

In general, the white ally community is systematically under-investing in the task of influencing skeptics, and this hasvery important social, institutional, and political consequences. If society is to implement racial equity initiatives with organizations or communities, it will be vital for more people who think of themselves as allies to have more frequent and effective conversations in the white community about whether anti-POC racism merits special attention.

The Ally Priorities Tool encourages allies to take a clear-eyed look at the energy and activities that comprise their anti-racism practice. In the instrument, a number of activities are presented that allies have said comprise their ally practice. The instrument encourages you to do a short thought experiment where you create the ideal ally who is still you. Then you take note of the most important and secondary priorities of your time.

After doing this thought experiment, you will see the same list of activities. This time, you are asked to indicate which are the most important and secondary focus of your ally time and energy. Some people have noticed disconnect between what they think they should be doing and what they are doing. Exploring these potential disconnects is the purpose of the instrument.

The instrument also includes two additional questions based on the same list; the second time, the context of the rating is for an ally organization. These questions are provided to assist an organization that supports allies or for a group of allies to have a conversation about their personal and collective priorities.

ALLY PRIORITIES RANKING TOOL

This tool explores 10 categories of behavior that white allies engage in because of their passion for racial equity/reconciliation/justice. They are all legitimate and important ways that a white person can express their passion for racial issues. Of course, we all have a finite amount of time, and we must sometimes make hard choices to live a balanced life.

The next two questions ask you to use discernment to assess both what you think should be happening and what you think actually is happening for you and for other white allies.

QUESTION 1

Looking at your own best feasible version of yourself at this stage of your journey as a white ally - and recognizing that all of these are important – please put an H next to the three activity dimensions that you think SHOULD BE highest priority for you, and an M next to the two dimensions that SHOULD BE next two highest priority areas for you?

1. Efforts to create moments of the "beloved community" that includes fellowship between whites and people of color not based on accomplishing a task	
2. Serving as a collaborative leader with POC while working for institutional change	
3. Working on my personal interaction with POCs so that my behavior does not reflect white privilege	
4. Giving and getting peer support from other white allies	
5. Intervening when you witness racially problematic statements/behaviors	
6. Persuading white non-allies that racism is an important problem	
7. Managing your own learning path as an ally through media/ book/art consumption	
8. Making lifestyle/personal choices that reflect your passion for racial equity	
9. Supporting racial equity efforts with money or time	
10. Managing your online presence to promote racism consciousness	

QUESTION 2

Imagine that an objective assessment is being made of the focus of your white ally work. Looking at your actual behavior, use the same scale of H and M to indicate what the observer would say ACTUALLY ARE the 3 highest (H) and the next two most important (M) priorities of your white ally activity.

1.	Efforts to create moments of the "beloved community" that includes fellowship between whites and people of color not based on accomplishing a task	
2.	Serving as a collaborative leader with POC while working for institutional change	
3.	Working on my personal interaction with POCs so that my behavior does not reflect white privilege	
4.	Giving and getting peer support from other white allies	
5.	Intervening when you witness racially problematic statements/behaviors	
6.	Persuading white non-allies that racism is an important problem	
7.	Managing your own learning path as an ally through media/ book/art consumption	
8.	Making lifestyle/personal choices that reflect your passion for racial equity	
9.	Supporting racial equity efforts with money or time	
10.	Managing your online presence to promote racism consciousness	

SOME REFLECTION QUESTIONS FOR INDIVIDUALS

- Were there activities that you engage in that did not fit well into the categories provided?

- What are the biggest disconnects between the activities that your ideal ally self would be doing and what you are actually spending your time and energy on? What are the drivers of this disconnect?

- How motivated are you to make adjustments? What are examples of new choices you would need to make?

The following questions are primarily aimed at people who are involved in formal or informal groups of white allies trying to make a difference about racism.

QUESTION 3

Think about others you can reasonably call a group of allies; it may be an official ally organization or an unofficial one you have formed or are forming. If you could wave a magic wand and folks would adjust how the community of allies spend their time, what are the three areas that you think should get the most focus (H), and the next two areas that need secondary focus (M).

1.	Efforts to create moments of the "beloved community" that includes fellowship between whites and people of color not based on accomplishing a task	
2.	Serving as a collaborative leader with POC while working for institutional change	
3.	Working on my personal interaction with POCs so that my behavior does not reflect white privilege	
4.	Giving and getting peer support from other white allies	
5.	Intervening when you witness racially problematic statements/behaviors	
6.	Persuading white non-allies that racism is an important problem	
7.	Managing your own learning path as an ally through media/book/art consumption	
8.	Making lifestyle/personal choices that reflect your passion for racial equity	
9.	Supporting racial equity efforts with money or time	
10.	Managing your online presence to promote racism consciousness	

QUESTION 4

Looking at what your white ally group is actually doing these days- and recognizing that all of these are important – please put an H next to the three activity dimensions that you think actually are the highest priority for your group, and an M next to the two dimensions that are the next two highest priority areas for your group?

(Don't get distracted by the fact that group efforts inevitably entail time to execute. For example, if a group is mobilizing dozens of people for a protest, there are tasks needed to accomplish that goal which are not on list. For the sake of this instrument, these administrative tasks are categorized as time spent on the strategic activity of supporting a protest.)

1. Efforts to create moments of the "beloved community" that includes fellowship between whites and people of color not based on accomplishing a task	
2. Serving as a collaborative leader with POC while working for institutional change	
3. Working on my personal interaction with POCs so that my behavior does not reflect white privilege	
4. Giving and getting peer support from other white allies	
5. Intervening when you witness racially problematic statements/behaviors	
6. Persuading white non-allies that racism is an important problem	
7. Managing your own learning path as an ally through media/book/art consumption	
8. Making lifestyle/personal choices that reflect your passion for racial equity	
9. Supporting racial equity efforts with money or time	
10. Managing your on-line presence to promote racism consciousness	

WHY WHITE ALLIES MUST TAKE OVER THE WORK OF "WOKING"

ARGUMENTS FROM SOCIAL PSYCHOLOGY AND COGNITIVE SCIENCE

The multiple decades of racial dialogue work undergirding this project has led to the conclusion that the best way to change and expand a skeptic's view on race is to first engage in empathetic listening. In addition, there is a growing body of scientific evidence that shows, to the extent that a change in people's views can be catalyzed, empathy-based dialogue is the way to go. According to this research, the best way to foster "de-biasing" is to first listen empathetically to someone so they feel heard, and after that, raise experiences and facts that invite them to a broader and more nuanced perspective. As one journalist titled a review of this research: "Research says there are ways to reduce racial bias. Calling people racist is not one of them."[3]

Social scientists who study influence would also advise that aggressively calling out someone who has said racially-problematic things is not the only action that an ally may want to refrain from if their intention is to maximize influence. Scholars of social psychology have strong evidence about the existence of a dynamic called the Backfire Effect. This term describes what happens when people are confronted with facts that challenge their views. In a remarkably high percentage of circumstance, their response—no matter how esteemed the source—is to double down on their beliefs and find some rationale for dismissing this new information.

3 https://www.vox.com/identities/2016/11/15/13595508/racism-trump-research-study

(These days, accusing others of dispensing "fake news" is often what this strategy looks like.)

Those who study the Backfire Effect list a number of steps for trying to influence people when you know that facts are not likely to work. One expert suggests these steps.[4]

- Discuss, don't attack (no ad hominem and no ad Hitlerum),
- Listen carefully and try to articulate the other position accurately,
- Show respect,
- Acknowledge that you understand why someone might hold that opinion, and
- Try to show how changing facts does not necessarily mean changing worldviews.

Julia Galef, head of the Center for Applied Rationality, offers this advice:

> "One important mental shift that I and other people have found really useful in remaining fair minded and objective in arguments is instead of thinking about the argument as a battle where you're trying to win, reframe it in your mind so that you think of it as a partnership, a collaboration in which the two of you together or the group of you together are trying to figure out the right answer."[5]

The conclusion by persuasion researchers that attacking someone is unlikely to change their minds is bolstered by people who study neurobiology. Many researchers have found that the circuitry in our brains that is activated when humans feel under physical threat, is also activated when we believe our worldview is being attacked.[6] TThus, telling someone that their viewpoint is the same as that of someone they see as morally inferior (e.g. "Your views are clearly racist!") is likely to be perceived

4 https://www.scientificamerican.com/article/how-to-convince-someone-when-facts-fail/

5 http://bigthink.com/in-their-own-words/the-key-to-rational-argument-reframe-it-as-a-partnership

6 https://boingboing.net/2017/01/17/the-neuroscience-of-changing-y.html

in the brain as telling them that you are about to hurt them physically. Often, people's fight or flight responses will be activated, including the adrenaline and other chemicals that our body has evolved to help us mount counterattacks when we are threatened.

This is not to say that lambasting someone's racist point of view does not feel good, and can provide an effective release valve for us. Such diatribes may even be persuasive with onlookers. Sadly though, there is good evidence that such strategies have very little chance of working with the person you are talking to.

Social psychology and cognitive science are not the only disciplines that have come to similar conclusions about persuasion and influence. Many experts in diplomacy and conflict resolution – where the capacity to influence others is a critical skill – say that being able to listen empathetically to people you sharply disagree with can be vital when moving them to one's own position.

EXTENDING DIGNITY

Harvard scholar Donna Hicks, who has done diplomatic and conflict resolution work around the world, says that granting people you disagree with dignity is very important when trying to influence them. "Dignity is the desire to be treated well. It is an unspoken human yearning that is at the heart of all conflicts, yet no one is paying attention to it," she says. Hicks' years of experience taught her that the key to shifting people to a mindset of collaborative problem solving around an ongoing conflict is to make them feel that their dignity is being acknowledged by the other side. Yet all too often, people who are trying to engage others fail to do this, even as they themselves feel anger or hurt because they have not been afforded dignity by the other party.

But what exactly is this dignity that you are supposed to grant to people you disagree with in order to influence them? One definition of dignity is "the quality of being worthy of esteem or respect." Hicks goes further, and says that dignity actually has 10 component elements, each associated with what we must do so that others feel that their dignity is recognized. The following is taken almost directly from an article by Hicks.

- **Acceptance of Identity**—Approach people as neither inferior nor superior to you; assume they have integrity.
- **Recognition—**Validate others for their talents, hard work, thoughtfulness, and help; give credit to others for their contributions, ideas and experience.
- **Acknowledgment—**Give people your full attention by listening, hearing, validating and responding to their concerns and what they have been through.
- **Inclusion—**Make others feel that they belong at all levels of relationship (family, community, organization, nation).
- **Safety—**Put people at ease at two levels: physically, where they feel free of bodily harm; and psychologically, where they feel free of concern about being shamed or humiliated, that they feel free to speak without fear of retribution.
- **Fairness—**Treat people justly, with equality, and in an even-handed way, according to agreed-upon laws and rules.
- **Independence—**Empower people to act on their own behalf so that they feel in control of their lives and experience a sense of hope and possibility.
- **Understanding—**Believe that what others think matters; give them the chance to explain their perspectives, and express their points of view; actively listen in order to understand them.
- **Benefit of the Doubt—**Treat people as trustworthy; start with the premise that others have good motives and are acting with integrity.
- **Accountability—**Take responsibility for your actions; if you have violated the dignity of another, apologize; make a commitment to change hurtful behaviors.

THE IRONIES OF EXTENDING DIGNITY

If we apply these concepts at the societal level, it is easy to see racism undermines the dignity of POC in all of the ten elements. If we apply this analysis to interpersonal racism – especially the conscious kind – the result is not much different.

However, what Hicks and similar experts say about the importance of granting dignity leads to an ironic conclusion about those who deny racism. It may very well be that, although racism directly subverts the dignity of POC, it takes extending dignity to people who question the reality of racism in order to eliminate racism.

Regardless of whether we think it is reasonable or not, both progressives and conservatives have produced a racial discourse in which racism skeptics often feel that their dignity is undermined. This results in a white fragility that is so extreme, that virtually any suggestion that a white skeptic is connected to historical or current racism causes extreme reactions, shutting down, and disengagement.

> Drawing white folks out so they can examine and potentially revisit their views should be white people's work.

Without question, a lot of this is caused by white racism skeptics and people with racist views. This apparent white fragility – especially as it plays out in the media – is a cynical attempt to undermine racial progress by limiting any discussion of societal accountability for racism. If anti-racists mention racism, many non-progressives accuse them of "playing the race card" or being "the real racists." This is a clever and convenient result that the forces of racial retrenchment have collectively created.

But it is also true that the behavior of anti-racist activists toward racism skeptics has often been dismissive, condescending, and lacking respect. With respect to the issue of dignity, anti-racist activists have often violated several of the key ways to afford dignity to skeptics in discourse about racism. Members of the anti-racism movement must ask themselves hard questions, most importantly: How frequently do we fail to grant dignity to racial conservatives when talking about race? Arguably, several dimensions of the 10 elements are commonly denied those who hold racially conservative views. (Most frequently denied are Acceptance of Identity, Acknowledgment, Safety, Understanding, and Benefit of the Doubt.)

> Reading a run of the mill skeptic/racist the critical race theory riot act for their unsophisticated racial views seems rather like an emotional indulgence that does not serve the cause of racial equity.

It is understandable why an anti- racist advocate – particularly one who is a POC - might be disinclined to spend energy affording dignity to a racism skeptic. Why should an anti-racist advocate give understanding to someone who denies a basic reality of life that affects millions of people? Why should they give the benefit of the doubt to someone who denies that racism exists? The ally knows that modern racism often works below the conscious awareness of the person who is racist. For that matter, why should they give psychological safety to those who deny racism, when their racially-backwards beliefs are part of a system that is designed to withhold both psychological and physical safety from millions of others?

It is also understandable why an anti-racist activist of color may choose to not push themselves past these questions. Their lives are stressful enough simply coping with the task of surviving racism. Why should it be their responsibility to be empathetic when listening to views that hurt them directly? Furthermore, when anti-racist advocates of color try to challenge racism skeptics' views on race, they are seen as self-interested, or even whiners. Because of perceptions like this, many anti-racism advocates increasingly regard spending time trying to influence skeptics as a fruitless endeavor.

It is time to shift the work of changing hearts and minds of racism skeptics away from people of color and onto white allies. They are perceived as having more credibility by racism skeptics, not only because they are white, but also because they are not seen as advocating for themselves. Their dignity is not as directly undermined by racism as is that of POC.

It is useful to remember that as a white person, you are in a much better position to interact with racism skeptics with a listening-based strategy than are POC. On a daily basis, POC must endure the indirect impact of white skepticism that racism really matters, and they must do so as they are they are experiencing overt and subtle racism in their lives. As you may have heard from POC in the past, the natural emotional reaction to this spans a broad range that includes irritation, rage, depression, and feeling gaslighted[7] by the majority population.

Some POC might choose to have conversations where white people's racial skepticism is consciously expressed. That is great for those who want to engage in this way. But it would not be fair for society to expect POC to endure this. POC have enough of a burden just coping with the results of this skepticism every day. Drawing white folks out so they can examine and potentially revisit their views should be white folks' work.

Many passionate white allies argue that it is not their moral obligation to respond aggressively to people who, at this late stage in the anti-racism struggle, express views that are either explicitly racist or demonstrate they have chosen to remain blissfully ignorant about the realities of racism. While passion and empathy with POC at the root of that outrage is appreciated, this project flips that argument around. **Specifically, a white person indulging in verbal outrage toward anyone but the most**

7 Gaslighting - manipulating someone by psychological means into questioning their own sanity

unreconstructed racist is, in fact, an act of white privilege.

What POC need is for white allies to be focused on using their common whiteness with racism skeptics/racists – except perhaps virulent ones – and the tools in the workbook to reach racism skeptics. While allies may be energized by the ritual of verbally blasting whites who are not sufficiently woke, the question must be asked: Is such an exchange doing anything to reduce the amount of racism that POC are facing? White allies who are interacting with skeptics are not having their core personhood challenged; they are not being insulted, as a person of color might be in the same situation. Given that, reading a run-of-the-mill skeptic/racist the "critical race theory riot act" for their unsophisticated racial views seems rather like an emotional indulgence that does not serve the cause of racial equity.

Undoubtedly, it takes a great deal of emotional and even spiritual discipline to extend dignity to people who are demonstrating racist views. It is natural to want to throttle them verbally, and perhaps physically. But the discipline of resisting this lashing out at racists for the sake of greater goals is the work that POC have had to do for hundreds of years. It is now time for white allies to take on this work, even though it does not feel good.

In addition, it is likely that you as a white ally are more capable of getting white people to be honest about their views on race and racism. Remember, a significant proportion of white people are willing to express to anonymous surveyors that they think POC are some version of inferior-- less intelligent, more criminally-minded, lazy, or otherwise less than white.[8] Only the most brazen racists don't have the couth to hide these views from POC in conversation. Clearly though, to the extent that anyone can draw out the candid beliefs of racism skeptics as well as overt racists – and these beliefs are best brought out in the open if they are to ever change – it is white allies, equipped with proven communications strategies of empathetic listening.

8 For example, a 2014 study the University of Illinois found that about 22 percent of whites think that whites are more intelligent than blacks and 33 percent reported thinking that blacks are less hardworking. http://igpa.uillinois.edu/programs/racial-attitudes

Essentially, it is the task of white allies to use their privileged status and consistently do the very hard work of recognizing skeptics' dignity so that they can help them see how they, the skeptics, are denying dignity to others.

LISTENING SELF-ASSESSMENT TOOLS

As noted, empathetic listening is foundational to methods of engagement advocated in this workbook. It is important that you take an honest self-assessment of your tendencies, habits, and capacities around listening. This lesson includes four instruments that encourage you to reflect on your listening – when you have done it well and poorly, and when the conversation involved race and when it did not. Engage these assessment forms when you are able to take sufficient time in probing your memory, writing, and making sense of what you wrote and remember.

You are encouraged to complete all the forms, but be prepared for the fact that this may take a fair amount of time. The exercises are designed to help you think more deeply about your listening behavior so that you can become a more intentional listener. If you engage these forms, you take a few trips down memory lane to recall important internal and external subtleties of several past situations. Of course, you have the option of just reading through the exercise instructions and not actually doing them. As you consider how much to engage the exercises, remember that becoming a better listener will not only help your work as a white ally against racism, but will also help you in other realms where listening matters, which is virtually everywhere.

After the reflection forms, there will be brief review of listening best practices that other people have found to be useful. You are encouraged to experiment with these and refine what works best for you.

The four listening self-assessment forms are as follows:

WORKSHEET 1 - SUCCESSES IN NON-RACIAL EMPATHETIC LISTENING

WORKSHEET 2 - FAILURES IN NON-RACIAL EMPATHETIC LISTENING

WORKSHEET 3 - EMOTIONS DURING FAILURES IN RACE CONVERSATIONS

WORKSHEET 4 - SITUATIONAL FACTORS IN RACE CONVERSATION SUCCESSES

Preamble to Worksheet 1 – The questions in Worksheet 1 review a few aspects of yourself that may have contributed to the results you experienced in your previous attempts at empathetic listening.

WORKSHEET 1: SUCCESSES IN NON-RACIAL EMPATHETIC LISTENING

Think of 2-3 times when you think you were successful at empathetic listening on a difficult topic, not necessarily related to race. To clarify your separate memories, name each of the times.

Successful listening episode 1

____

Successful listening episode 2

____

Successful listening episode 3

____

For the rest of this worksheet, try to remember some specific circumstances of each of these episodes. Be especially attentive to commonalities between the episodes.

How would you describe what you were doing physically: posture, breathing, etc.?

____

____

____

____

____

____

What was your emotional state going into the situation(s)? How were you feeling during it?

What kinds of thoughts were you having that were the backdrop to the content of the conversation(s)? What was your conscious intention in the encounter?

How would you describe your verbal behavior? Your speaking style, tone, and pace of speech? Were there some words or phrases you used more or less than usual?

Post-Script to Worksheet 1 – Whether the topic is about race or not, it is important to be aware of what behaviors in various dimensions support our success. Sometimes, if we catch ourselves doing things that are associated with poor listening, we can shift to better listening just by changing to behaviors that we do when we are successful.

Preamble to Worksheet 2 - In order to improve your listening practice, it is important to work on your skill in re-examining listening episodes. It is most important to honestly examine your behavior, and its effect on both you and the other person.

WORKSHEET 2: FAILURES IN NON-RACIAL EMPATHETIC LISTENING

Think of a 1-2 times when you were unsuccessful at empathetic listening on a difficult topic, not necessarily related to race.

Unsuccessful listening Episode 1

____

Unsuccessful listening Episode 2

____

How would you describe what you were doing physically: posture, breathing, etc.?

____

____

____

____

____

____

____

What was your emotional state going into the situation(s)? How were you feeling during it?

____

____

____

What kinds of thoughts were you having that were the backdrop to the content of the conversation(s)? What was your conscious intention in the encounter?

How would you describe your verbal behavior? Your speaking style, tone, and pace of speech? Were there some words or phrases you used more or less than usual?

Post-Script to Worksheet 2 - Take a moment to review Worksheets 1 and2. If there are some significant contrasts in the answers to the questions about successes and failures, you should pay special attention. Many people create success by being mindful of the subtle decisions they make about their body, thoughts, and emotions, and trying to make conscious choices that are associated with successful outcomes.

Preamble to Worksheet 3 – This form helps you pay attention to how you behave in unproductive exchanges about race with racism skeptics. (A productive exchange is one in which: 1) the ally gets to be their authentic self in a significant part of the encounter, and 2) the skeptic leaves the encounter with some level of interest in talking to the ally about race in the future. The focus is on the comments that serve as emotional triggers and that make it difficult to stay centered and in a mode of empathetic listening.

Worksheet 3 helps you reflect on how racist or racism-skeptical statements might affect you in a way that undermines your listening. Here is a list of common racism-denying statements..

- "Racism means having intentionally negative views of other groups. So if I don't have conscious negative intent, I don't have to worry about being racist."
- "Nowadays, there are very few advantages to being white. I am not privileged."
- "Very few people are consciously racist anymore."
- "Slavery and segregation were a long time ago. We should not talk about them anymore and just move on."
- "The economic problems of people of color are primarily due to the bad choices that they make."
- "If people of color would just act properly, law enforcement would treat them fairly."
- "It is vital that America drastically reduce the level of immigration so that we can return to our cultural greatness."
- "Those athletes and others protesting should be grateful they live in America and should not disrespect the nation and the flag by kneeling during the National Anthem. "

Feel free to focus on other racism-skeptical statements, if they are more likely to prevent you from an empathetic listening response.

WORKSHEET 3: EMOTIONS DURING FAILURES IN RACE CONVERSATIONS

After reviewing the list of racism-denying statements that bug you, list the comments that most push you off-center. If the sentiment that you want to focus on is not on the list, add it.

- "Racism means having intentionally negative views of other groups. I am colorblind. So if I don't have conscious negative intent, I don't have to worry about being racist."
- "Nowadays, there are very few advantages to being white. I am not privileged".
- "Very few people are consciously racist anymore."
- "Slavery and segregation were a long time ago. We should not talk about them anymore and just move on."
- "The economic problems of people of color are primarily due to the bad choices that they make."
- "If people of color would just act properly, law enforcement would treat them fairly."
- "It is vital that America drastically reduce the level immigration so that we can return to our cultural greatness."
- "Those athletes and others protesting should be grateful they live in America and should not disrespect the nation and the flag by kneeling during the National Anthem. "

- ____
- ____
- ____

What are the statements that make it most difficult for you to engage the skeptic from a place that is centered?

1. ____

____

2. ____

____

3. ____

____

Think back to specific episodes when you heard the statements you listed above, and you were not able to stay centered maintaining a practice of listening. Give the incident a name to help focus your memory work.

Episode name	Statement
1.	
2.	
3.	

Here are some examples of the emotions that white allies have said they feel in the face of some statements and also some of the underlying reasons behind those feelings.

Emotion	Reason
ANGRY	...that someone who shares my name could be so stupid.
FRUSTRATED	...that someone who claims Christianity could be so unloving.
SAD	...that this person is clearly cutting themselves off from many good people.
OVERWHELMED	...at all of the conversational work that this person needs.
IRRITATED	...that I have to have this conversation again.
FATIGUED	...that so many white folks have learned so little.
SHAME	...that I used to feel like that and have only recently awakened to reality.

Post-Script to Worksheet 3 – In order to improve your skills as an effective listener, it is useful to put space between the skeptic's statement and your intense emotional response. One way to do this is to consciously re-visit the linkages between a statement and its underlying impact on you. Having looked at this chain, you can remind yourself that there are other ways of thinking about the issue and hopefully break this unhelpful cycle.

Take for example, the hypothetical ally's emotion on the second line on the example table in the Worksheet 3. Here, the ally is frustrated at some racism-denying comments made by Christians because they seem unloving. To strengthen this ally's ability to stay centered, it might be useful to remind themselves they know that many Christians are unloving and they accept this daily. Then the ally can make a decision to replicate the way they accept this fact when race is not in the conversation. Similarly, they can spend some time thinking about a new question: Why do racist remarks make it harder to accept that some Christians are unloving, than to accept this is true when race is not involved?

By going down either of these roads of reflection, the hypothetical ally is reminding themselves that their reaction is not inevitable. That is the ultimate goal of the entire reflective enterprise – to encourage you to describe your internal process and reflect on it with a slight bit of distance. The hope is you will be better prepared so that the next time a similar situation arises, you can manage yourself with greater intention and effectiveness.

Preamble to Worksheet 4 – Most white allies have had at least a few experiences where a skeptic said or did something that was racist or racially-problematic, and the ally was able to invite the skeptic into a productive conversation to reevaluate their point of view. Even if these situations have been rare, it is useful to learn lessons from them by asking yourself a few reflection questions.

The success of the situation is typically affected by circumstances that are largely environmental and/or that the ally cannot control. Perhaps the environment was more conversational and relaxed. Perhaps someone had previously set the tone of an attitude of inquiry. Maybe bad weather had trapped people in the space, so that people had to settle in and talk to each other.

Undoubtedly, there were personal factors that made a difference. Perhaps you had just come from the gym, so your endorphins were engaged. Perhaps you had just gotten some good news. Maybe it was a party, and you had just the right amount of snacks or alcohol, whatever level that is for you.

The point of these instruments is to consider which internal and external factors tend to support your effectiveness.

WORKSHEET 4:
SITUATIONAL FACTORS IN RACE CONVERSATION SUCCESSES

Think of two different experiences in which you turned a racially-problematic moment with a skeptic into a productive dialogue.

	Experience 1	Experience 2
What was the situation?		
Some factors you had little influence over that likely helped?		
Factors that you had significant influence over that likely helped?		

Using the previous table as example input, try to remember each episode in more detail, and try to make sense of your what emotions came up for you in wake of the racist/racism denying behavior your observed.

Statement	Emotion	Reason
1.		
2.		
3.		

Were there any physical factors in the situation, from your choices or factors beyond your control, which you think contributed to your success?

Were there any decisions you made about what you were paying attention to in thought or emotion that helped you stay centered in the conversation?

Post-Script to Worksheet 4 – If you are reading this after filling out all four forms...congratulations! Kudos for translating your commitment to better allyship into the energy necessary for a very extensive reflection process.

To fully capitalize on your efforts, it might be helpful to review the four worksheets, and think about three broad questions:

1. Looking at your body, mind, and emotions, what are the things that you should pay attention to and affirmatively do, to maximize your chance of staying in an empathetic listening mode?

2. Looking at your body, mind, and emotions, what are the decisions you should try to avoid making, so that you can be most effective?

3. Are there situational factors outside of your control that you should be aware of because they impact your effectiveness?

CREATING YOUR LISTENING BEST PRACTICES TOOL

In addition to doing your own reflection, you can benefit from learning from other people's best practices for becoming a better listener. You may want to experiment with integrating some of these methods into your own listening practices, while taking note of which ones are helpful and which are not.

Note: Listening experts point out that there is a lack of general appreciation for the fact that good listening requires advance preparation. Kai Degner of the Listening Corps (www.listeningcorps.com) points out that while many know that one should prepare to speak to people, very few recognize that it can be equally important to prepare to listen. J. Scott Wagner, author of A Liberal's Guide to Conservatives (strongly recommended for white allies!) also advises that you consciously prepare for situations that you know will test your listening skills. The act of envisioning yourself having a successful listening session can help. Three things to focus on are:

1. Reminding yourself that you can listen effectively and stay centered;
2. Envisioning how the session will go, and how you will feel and behave within it;
3. Reminding yourself that listening empathetically to views you disagree with does not means that you agree with those views.

One method of strengthening your listening is to consciously separate strategies into three parts: your values, your physical body, and your attention/thoughts.

TACTICS BASED ON FOCUSING ON VALUES THAT MATTER TO YOU

Degner asserts that anyone attempting to maintain a high level of listening throughout an encounter should recognize they will inevitably have to contend with what he calls "listening blocks". These are factors within the listener or within the environment that can get in the way of listening; they can vary from a distracting air conditioner noise to a persistent thought that the person you are talking to looks like someone from your past who rubbed you the wrong way.

Degner suggests that when listening blocks emerge, one general strategy is to emotionally/mentally refocus on one of three values that, in preparation for the session, you committed to. These three values - empathy, curiosity, and patience – have listeners reground themselves when they stray from the path of empathetic listening. Some questions that you might ask that relate to these values are:

Empathy: Is there a positive intent in the person that I can connect to?
Curiosity: Is there a perspective within the person's point of view that I need to understand more?
Patience: How can I extend to the skeptic the same willingness to stay engaged that I would want if someone became distracted while listening to me?

MIND-BODY TACTICS

Some white allies have found that a good way to re-center when their attention drifts, is focus on the mind-body connection and to make adjustments that are associated with success in listening. It helps if you have mentally prepared to call on this action for this purpose. Some examples of helpful actions that white allies have used include:

- Biting your lip
- Touching your tongue to the roof of your mouth

- Shifting your position to one that is more relaxed
- Taking deeper breaths
- Keeping your eyes focused on the speaker's eyes
- Envisioning there is super-glue on your lips preventing you from talking
- Keeping your eyes focused on the speaker's mouth

Your objective is to examine if there are any choices in managing your body that help you become more effective. What mind-body strategies do you think (or have found) are most effective in helping you stay in empathetic listening mode?

1. ______________________________

2. ______________________________

3. ______________________________

ATTENTION-BASED TACTICS - LISTENING FOR X

Degner says that apart from focusing on your body or on your values, another strategy is to enhance your mindfulness about what you are listening for. He calls the strategy "Listening for X." The first step is remembering what you listened for in situations it was effective. The idea is that listening blocks happen because at key moments, the listener is paying excess attention to the possibility of some specific idea being raised, and as a result misses other important information in the conversation.

This exercise is especially important for white anti-racist allies. In conversation with racism skeptics, white allies are often paying special note (i.e. listening for) something the skeptic might say that reflects racially-problematic beliefs, whether they are deep-seated, conscious, or based around ignorance. In fact, for many allies, a core part of their personal practice is to monitor language and publicly call out people as white supremacists when they say problematic things.

Even in less extreme cases, there are still patterns in what allies are often listening for during encounters with racism skeptics (or other allies). These can include:

- Evidence of beliefs about POC inferiority
- Beliefs that reflect unacknowledged white privilege
- Inaccurate understandings of how racism works
- Deficits in empathy or compassion for people of color
- Ignorance of key facts in American history
- Conservative political ideology
- Evidence that the skeptic is more racist than they think of themselves

This is just a partial list. A common element in all of them is that the listener judges the other person as wrong and requiring correction.

It is important to be as honest with yourself as possible about what you might be listening for that undermines your capacity to empathetically listen to skeptics. Think about settings in which you have not been successful in empathetically listening.

In conversations about race with other white people, what do you listen for that sometime impedes your ability to stay in a stance of empathetic listening?

1. ______________________________

____

2. ______________________________

____

3. ______________________________

____

To be clear, you are not wrong for listening for these things. As you grow in your lifelong journey of allyship, it is actually useful for you to listen for the various ways that racial skepticism manifests. You need to be listening for the ways that the existing system of entrenched racial hierarchies affects people's thoughts, feelings, and actions. Any conversation is a chance to learn about how resistance to racial equity is held together within the thoughts, feelings, and perspectives of a skeptic.

You must also be listening for other things. If you want to take people on a journey of collaborative dialogue that might expand their outlook, you may need to shift your focus, or at least expand it. If you want to have a reasonable chance of moving a skeptic, you will need to listen for additional things that are very different than the above. Fruitful possibilities include:

- Experiences that are similar to ones you have had
- Things you can agree with
- Underlying needs embedded within what the person is saying
- Potential openings for future conversation

The space below is for any summary notes about your own listening practice.

THE WHITE ALLY RESPONSE ASSESSMENT TOOL

SELF-ASSESSMENT: RESPONDING TO RACIALLY PROBLEMATIC STATEMENTS AND SITUATIONS

This instrument assesses what happens in your heart, mind, and behavior when racially-problematic statements or behaviors happen in your presence.

Think about your reaction when people do or say things that your find racially troubling. Here are some examples of statements.

- "Racism means having intentionally negative views of other groups. I am colorblind. So if I don't have conscious negative intent, I don't have to worry about being racist."
- "Nowadays, there are very few advantages to being white. I am not privileged."
- "Very few people are consciously racist anymore."
- "Slavery and segregation were a long time ago. We should not talk about them anymore and just move on."
- "The economic problems of people of color are primarily due to the bad choices that they make."
- "If people of color would just act properly, law enforcement would treat them fairly."
- "It is vital that America drastically reduce the level immigration so that we can return to our cultural greatness."
- "Those athletes and others protesting should be grateful they live in America and should not disrespect the nation and the flag by kneeling during the National Anthem. "

You will assess your reaction to hearing statements like this in two ways:

Dimension 1: What happens in your heart and mind? How often do you have a visceral response – whether you show it or not – when racially-problematic statements are made in your presence?

- If you have a visceral reaction 2/3 of the time or more, your score is 3
- If you have a visceral reaction between 1/2 and 2/3 of the time, your score is 10
- If you have a visceral reaction less than 1/3 of the time, your score is 20.

Write your visceral response score here: ______________________________

Dimension 2: What happens with respect to your actual behavior? How often do you engage the person who has made the racially-problematic statements?

- If you engage the person and the situation more than 2/3 of the time, you score is 100
- If you engage the person/situation less than 2/3 of the time, your score is 20.

Write your behavioral response score here: ___________________________

Add together the our overall response score here: ______________________

- If your score is 120, you are an Undercover Spy in Training / Zen Activist
- If your score is 110 or 30, you are a Reservist / Contextual Player
- If your score is 103, you are a Cavalry / First Responder
- If your score is 40, you are an Analyst / Quiet Observer
- If your score is 23, you are a Scout / Mental Warrior

THE CAVALRY . . . AKA THE FIRST RESPONDERS

DIAGNOSIS

You've got to love these folks...When it comes to expressions of racial skepticism, they are like the Cavalry or First Responders – they may not clearly see the path forward, but their prime directive is to act. They often have to manage a strong internal reaction, and they really don't understand where skeptics are coming from. Regardless, they consistently engage--sometimes with a well-developed plan, but sometimes without one.

When a racism-skeptic reveals himself or herself, Cavalry/First Responders feel a big gulf that sometimes causes a sinking feeling in their gut. It is very hard for them to understand this type of thinking, and hearing it often triggers them emotionally. Many manage this situation well enough that their internal tribulation is largely hidden from the other person. Other members of the Cavalry are less opaque with their feelings, and their reaction is apparent. But no matter how well they manage their emotions, engaging is a lot of work since they have very little understanding or empathy for this way of thinking. It just seems forcign to them! And the idea of having understanding or empathy for this point of view itself seems weird.

In their minds, the most important thing to do when bumping against people denying of racism is to counter it, and so they do - almost every time.

PRESCRIPTION

Since these people are already consistently engaging, they don't need coaching for increased action. For them, the primary growth edge is to focus on greater effectiveness. A good place to start is getting a better handle on their internal response. Getting a better grip on themselves when they hear racially-problematic statements is likely to be a challenge, since they don't understand racism skeptical thinking, and it creates a visceral reaction in them. Often they don't want to understand it, since that can feel like a concession and a granting of legitimacy.

GROWTH EDGE QUESTIONS FOR CAVALRY/FIRST RESPONDERS

For Managing Emotions

1. How long have racism-denying statements by other whites really gotten to you emotionally?
2. If there was ever a time when this did not happen, what changed?
3. Are there past people or situations that your mind subtly goes to when you are triggered?
4. In other situations not related to race, what strategies have you found useful in managing your emotions in the face of behavior that really bothers you?

For Understanding and Empathy

1. Now you respond to racial skepticism like a firefighter putting out a small fire before it grows. How would it feel, every so often, to meet racial skepticism like a spy who asks innocent questions so you can be more effective the next time?
2. Can you reconnect with the empathy you have felt in the past for someone with racially skeptical views? Has anyone you deeply loved held these views? Can you remember feeling at least one racially skeptical view yourself?
3. Have you asked any other allies about books, movies, or videos that helped them better understand racially skeptical thinking?

THE SCOUTS . . . AKA THE MENTAL WARRIORS

DIAGNOSIS

Racism-denying statements *really* bug these folks. They don't understand or empathize with this thinking. Even though they may seethe or get very sad internally when such statements are made, these folks tend toward caution with engaging skeptics. They don't have a clear plan about what will be effective, and they don't want their reaction to hurt the moment or the relationship. As a result, they don't usually choose to engage the skeptic. When racism or racism-skeptical thinking emerges, the Scouts/ Mental Warriors often just inwardly shake their heads, sigh, and later report the difficult moment to people they trust.

The mistake Scouts/Mental Warriors most fear making is engaging poorly and thus reducing the chance that they or anyone else will ever move the needle with this person. The Mental Warriors have a strong sense that engaging poorly will undermine any chance of the skeptic changing their minds at any time.

PRESCRIPTION

The growth edge for Scouts/Mental Warriors is to figure out a way to engage more frequently and do so in a way that does not confirm their fears of backlash.

GROWTH EDGE QUESTIONS FOR SCOUTS/MENTAL WARRIORS

1. Can you recall a time when someone you loved (including yourself) thought like a racism skeptic?
2. What happens to your compassion for skeptics when you recall that American society is designed to keep racism hidden from white people?
3. Can you imagine now and then using race skepticism as a learning opportunity about not only what the skeptics think, but about your own ability to ask a non-judgmental question?

4. In other areas of life outside of race, what strategies have you found successful for engaging points of view that you find unattractive?
5. Think back to a time when a skeptic did/said something problematic and you did not engage. Imagine what might have happened if you engaged the skeptic with a non-judgmental question about what experiences made them feel like that.

THE RESERVISTS . . . AKA THE CONTEXTUAL PLAYERS

DIAGNOSIS

Reservists/Contextual Players have handles to help them engage skeptics with a good chance of having some impact. They often have reasonable understanding of where skeptics are coming from, and usually are not overly triggered. Sometimes they are flummoxed by the skeptic's response and other times triggered by it. Sometimes they stay centered and have an empathetic understanding, even though they think the skeptics are wrong. Many factors matter to both their internal reaction and their behavior, including their own mood and the setting.

Their behavior is highly dependent on what is happening inside of them, as well as factors in the situation. Overall though, like other ally types, they often have little confidence that their engagement – when it does happen – will produce positive results.

PRESCRIPTION

To improve their effectiveness, Contextual Players can focus on the reflective work needed to engage more frequently as well as on the analytical work to make their engagements more effective. The good news for them is that because they have a mixed response both in their thoughts/ feelings and in their behaviors, they can look to themselves to find useful lessons that might help them boost their weaknesses.

GROWTH EDGE QUESTIONS FOR CONTEXTUAL PLAYERS:

For Emotions and Understanding

1. For the situations in which you mostly understand and stay centered around racial skepticism, what are the keys reasons you are able to engage the way you do?
2. What would have to happen to apply those lessons to when you don't stay centered or don't engage?
3. What are the key differences between the situations that have to do with your thoughts and feelings, such as your level of compassion for the person, or your mood?

4. What are the key differences between the situations that are outside of you, such as the behavior itself, the kinds of people present, your perceptions about skeptic, or other factors?

For Effectiveness

1. What are my typical communication strategies? How effective am I at creating an encounter that feels authentic?
2. If I knew I would be rewarded for increasing my effectiveness with skeptics, what would I change about when and how I engaged them?

THE UNDERCOVER SPIES IN TRAINING... AKA THE ZEN ACTIVISTS

DIAGNOSIS

These folks, the Undercover Spies/Zen Activists of the anti-racist ally community, are rather infrequently triggered by expressions of racial skepticism. They usually have a keen understanding of where skeptics are coming from. Some Undercover Spies/Zen Activists have developed this understanding through a good deal of reading about how racism-skeptical thinking is a useful byproduct of a society that replicates racial hierarchies. Others have empathy for where skeptics are coming from because they have done a good deal of internal reflection and remember thinking like this. Still others can stay calm and not reactive because they have spent previous time sorting out how they could deeply love and generally respect people whose thoughts on race they find troubling.

Because Undercover Spies/Zen Activists stay centered and can connect with skeptics, they can often make strategic choices in guiding the conversation in ways that, over time, invite the skeptic to think differently without making them feel judged.

PRESCRIPTION

The primary thing these people should focus on is their effectiveness. The ambiguous nature of working with skeptics makes it hard to know if your engagements are doing anything, which also means it is easy to overestimate one's own impact. Since Undercover Spies/Zen Activists represent the people who are at the pinnacle of effort, they should also help other allies who are not at the same place in their ability to engage skeptics empathetically and strategically.

GROWTH EDGE QUESTIONS FOR ZEN ACTIVISTS/UNDERCOVER SPIES

1. What are things that I don't know about skeptic's thinking that I should ask about when engaging?

2. Could I improve the depth, breadth, and effectiveness of my storytelling when I engage skeptics? Are there experiences I can more effectively bring to bear from my past when I try to connect with skeptics?
3. Can I improve the questions I ask to get to the heart of the matter?
4. Are there risks that I am not taking when engaging skeptics that might help me become more effective?
5. What are some lessons about staying centered and coming from a place of empathy that I can pass on to other allies?

THE ANALYSTS . . . AKA THE QUIET OBSERVERS

DIAGNOSIS

You care about race relations and racial justice, but you are confused about what your role or even the proper response at an emotional level. You know that there are a lot of people with messed up views, but it is unclear whether it is your place to address them. For some Analysts, it is unclear whether their restrained emotional response is something to be addressed.

PRESCRIPTION

These folks care about racial equity, but too frequently stay on the sidelines as detached observers. Their primary focus should be on going from inaction to action. If they make a decision to change their behavior, they can start by tuning in to what happens in their minds and body when they hear racially-problematic statements. Do they experience anger, sadness, or frustration? Even though they rarely have a visceral reaction, they may still have a subtle physical reaction that is a signal of their connection to this issue. After noticing this reaction, Analysts can it as a signal to themselves that it is time to engage.

GROWTH EDGE QUESTIONS FOR QUIET OBSERVERS:

1. To what extent is your emotional response on issues of race similar or different to your emotional reaction on other social issues you care about?
2. What is your fear of what would happen either inside you or within the situation if you were to engage people who make statements that you define as racially-problematic?

FINAL THOUGHTS FOR PART ONE

Now that you have done all or most of the exercises in this section, it is time to transition to a focus on which type of interventions with allies are most important to you. Part Two is designed to get you ready to engage a variety of racially-problematic statements that racism skeptics sometimes make. After reading the overview of Part Two, you may want to go directly to the statements you feel the most urgency to respond to. In time, you must develop strategies for addressing comments about unconscious bias and unearned racial advantage, since these specific issues are foundational to progress on white racial attitudes. But if you are more drawn to other modules initially because they come up more frequently or they just bug you more, feel free to prepare for those first. The primary problem is that allies too frequently ignore racism skeptical remarks or engage them combatively; from this project's perspective, the most important thing allies should do is to start engaging differently on some topic. So let your passions guide the sequence.

Instead of preparing to respond to unexpected racially troubling comments, some allies will want to focus on the task of intentionally taking a skeptic up a ladder of understanding. If this applies to you, consider skipping most of Part Two and going directly to Part Three (the Primer), which provides a curriculum comprising a suggested sequence of ideas to make the focus of conversations. You might consider reading the initial explanation of the RACE Method that comprises the first portion of Part Two, before skipping the rest. Even though the Primer does not use the RACE Method specifically, the materials reflect its sensibility and general approach. It focuses on creating a planned conversation that leverages active listening, empathy, and mutual storytelling.

Whether you read Parts Two and Three next, you should be sure to read the Odds and Ends section that is Part Four. There are several instruments that will deepen your practice, as well as some short essays that will help you prepare for difficult interactions with racism skeptics as well as other anti-racism allies.

PART TWO: USING THE RACE METHOD TO ENGAGE RACISM DENIAL

Part 2 of the book focuses on preparing you to address racially problematic statements that emerge from time to time.

THE RACE METHOD

This workbook is based on science that indicates that the best way to produce long-run changes in how skeptics think about race and racism is to invite them into an authentic dialogue. We suggest that you manage this dialogue in a way that is natural and flexible, but also in accord with a general sequence of phases that have been proven to be most effective. We are calling this method of managing conversations about race "the RACE Method". This term is an acronym representing a set of conversation phases (Reflect, Ask, Connect, Expand) that the ally should take before and during the conversation. In the preferred sequence, they are:

REFLECT – preparing to be in listening mode, and refreshing one's own personal stories
ASK – inquiring about the experiences that have led the skeptic to their beliefs
CONNECT –telling an anecdote that demonstrates some degree of similarity
EXPAND – telling an anecdote that invites an awareness of race/racism

As will be discussed, there are other optional processes (mini-steps) that an ally might bring to bear, such as addressing contradictions in the skeptic's thinking, or bringing to bear facts that support the ally's view. But these additional steps are not essential to the four major phases of the RACE Method.

Fundamentally, the RACE Method involves purposely shifting the conversation away from a clash of opinions and a battle of "facts" between allies and skeptics. Instead, the ally will create an experience-based inquiry of the issue at hand, where the ally and the skeptic begin their dialogue by trying to make sense of the world based on comparing experiences. Later in the set of exchanges - maybe on a different day - the conversation begins to include external information (statistics, mental models, references) relevant to the journey of inquiry.

This section focuses on providing you with materials for conversation with skeptics that start with racially-problematic statements the skeptic may have made. The practical advice is organized in separate modules focused on strategies to engage specific statements. All of the modules are based on the RACE Method. Of course, there will be times when the topic of race comes up in a way for which there is no module. Thus, it is important that you understand the basic structure of the RACE Method so that you can adapt to the situation at hand.

Some additional guidelines to be aware of:

- The RACE Method steps usually work best in the suggested sequence. In some cases, you may need to vary from the sequence.
- You should attempt to manage the dialogue so that it feels natural; in fact, some people may be put off if they sense that you are "running a program" on them.
- Furthermore, some skeptics will want to talk about "facts" before talking about experiences (potentially setting you bothup for an unproductive debate about facts), or may want to hear experiences that opened your eyes before you have shared experiences that show you have some similarities to them (potentially putting you and the skeptic at odds at the start of the conversation). You may have to subtly redirect the conversation flow now and then in order to keep personal experiences as a core tool for your joint effort to make sense of the topic.
- The more you practice the Method, the better you will make choices about when to vary the sequence.
- In preparation for using the Method with racism skeptics, you can practice the method with other allies.

Let's walk through the phases one at a time.

PHASE 1: REFLECT
PREPARE FOR THE CONVERSATION, AND CENTER YOURSELF IN THE MOMENT

There are two levels of reflection – one well before the encounter with a skeptic, and one at the start of it. In improving your practice as an ally, you should spend some time thinking about your listening blockages, your counter measures to stay balanced if you start engaging unproductively, your response patterns, and the anecdotes you might bring to bear. This type of reflection is what this workbook is for.

The second level of reflection occurs in the moment when a racism-denying or racist statement happens. You are likely to respond more effectively if you take a moment to compose yourself and quickly bring to mind things you have reflected on before, such as your listening challenges and relevant anecdotes. Some people can do it by taking a deep breath, while others may need to go to the bathroom, refresh their drink, or take a short break from the conversation. No matter which works for you, re-centering yourself through a moment of reflection leads to better outcomes when you engage.

After you have done some work to augment your general listening skills, there is additional reflective work about specific issues related to race and racism. Each module here has reflection questions that can prepare you for talking to skeptics. Since race is a very broad topic and you have had hundreds or thousands of experiences with it, this is not a one-time process. Just as POC are on a never- ending journey to become more effective at dealing with the varieties of racism, your journey as a white ally is also never-ending. As they say, it's a marathon, not a sprint.

You should think about which racism-denying statements you most want to engage a skeptic around, and prepare for them. The Modules below provide guidance about how to use the RACE Method with respect to specific statements. Over time, the number of statements that are addressed by this project (both the workbook and the website) will grow. Once you understand the basics, you can potentially follow the RACE

Method to create your own steps for navigating encounters with racism skeptics on additional topics.

KEY STEPS WITHIN THE REFLECT PHASE

1. It is useful to be specific as you prepare to respond to racially-problematic statements. For example, the two statements "White privilege does not exist" in contrast to "People of color create most of their own economic problems" may affect you very differently on an emotional level, and require different strategies of engagement through conversation.
2. In your pre-reflection, you should become aware of the self-management strategies you will need to call upon to stay in empathetic listening mode. These will help you during the Ask phase, when you need to be ready to hear perspectives that will likely bother you.
3. When a skeptic makes a racially-problematic statement, your goal is to identify something within it that you can align yourself with. Depending on the sentiment and your own history, your point of alignment may be that you used to think like that yourself. If that is untrue, you can look for something else that you do not totally disagree with. (For example: "Police treat everyone fairly" includes the obviously true statement, "All police are not bad." "People of color often face challenges because of bad choices," includes the obviously true statement, "Personal decisions matter to people's economic outcomes.")
4. With respect to a specific racially-troubling statement, jot some notes about one or two experiences that illustrate some aspect of the statement that you can agree with. These are stories you will tell during the Connect phase. It can be useful to think of these anecdotes as having a few elements, such as the set-up, the key moment, and the takeaway. This clear conception gives you the flexibility of telling the story at different durations (for example, 45 seconds versus 3 minutes) so you can adapt to different situations. Some allies even turn the practice of relaying their anecdotes into an important part of their anti-racist practice.

5. In addition to developing at least one Connect anecdote that will help a skeptic feel aligned with you, you will develop an Expand story that reflects your current awareness that racism is real and something that needs more attention. If your Connect story demonstrates that you formerly thought like the skeptic does now, it can be very useful for your Expand story (also known as the "But later, I realized" story) to capture a moment when your more enhanced understanding of race came into focus. If you do not have such a transformation story, your Expand might simply recount an experience that reflects your understanding of race/racism. It is best if your anecdote is something that happened to you personally, but it might be a second-hand experience from someone you trust. The critical thing is that it is compelling, and your takeaway is a reasonable lesson from the experience. As with the Connect, you may want to practice telling the story at different durations.
6. There are two optional additions to the Expand phase. One is to raise some underlying issues that may seem like contradictions to the skeptic but actually are not. This may be as simple as saying something like: "Maybe it's possible that 'the vast majority of cops have good intentions' and it's also true that 'unconscious bias still affects many cops.'" Getting clear about how you articulate seeming contradictions to foster a skeptic's understanding should be part of what you reflect on in preparation.
7. Another possibility with Expand is to add a few relevant facts that will support your perspective. You don't want to overload yourself with these facts, because doing so will push you to try to base your conversation strategy on their delivery. As we discussed in Part One, facts are only effective if the person is open-minded, and this may not happen until much later in your journey of dialogue with a skeptic.

PHASE 2: ASK

PROBE THE SKEPTIC FOR THEIR BELIEFS AND, MOST IMPORTANTANTLY, THE EXPERIENCES BEHIND THEIR BELIEFS

The overall goal of the Ask phase is to shift the skeptic's focus from their beliefs about race/racism to the experiences that are animating their beliefs. If they have made a racially-problematic statement – and you have decided to engage them, your goal is not primarily to rebut the remark, although you might overtly demur from it, depending on its severity. If you decide to try a moment of engagement, your first goal is to invite them to freely express as much of their authentic views about race as you are comfortable hearing. After a brief additional focus on their beliefs, your primary goal is to move through the skeptic's beliefs to focus on experiences that have founded their beliefs. These experiences may be long ago – like what they were taught growing up – or they might be events that have happened relatively recently.

One thing that is important to decide is how much you will push the skeptic to go beneath the surface of their beliefs. In considering this approach, it is important to keep in mind a harsh reality: a significant proportion of white people will tell anonymous pollsters on the telephone that they think that POC (especially blacks but also Hispanics) are some combination of intellectually inferior, innately criminal, or lazier than white people.[9]

Nowadays, people know that expressing these views will subject them to being accused of being a "racist," which is widely considered to be morally repugnant and socially unacceptable. The fact that large proportions of the white public hold these views of POC but rarely discuss them openly makes it extremely difficult to have an honest conversation about racial equity.

White allies are uniquely positioned to get skeptics to own up to beliefs that are troubling to the ideal of racial equity, and may be troubling even somewhat to the skeptic. But in any specific encounter, it does not make

9 For example, a 2014 study the University of Illinois found that about 22 percent of whites think that whites are more intelligent than blacks and 33 percent reported thinking that blacks are less hardworking. Citation: http://igpa.uillinois.edu/programs/racial-attitudes

sense for you to push them to express these underlying beliefs if you will only judge them after they do so. You need to make conscious choices about how deep you want to go. For two of the modules (law enforcement and economic opportunity) we provide probes and reflections to probe for these more deeply biased views.

It is not critical to go to these deeper places to effectively work with a skeptic on their racism-denying beliefs. There are people with racially progressive beliefs who hold deep-seated views about the inferiority of some groups of color.[10] This demonstrates that progress on beliefs about racism can be made even with those who hold views of POC they don't like to discuss. The most important thing is to not open up this door to deeper beliefs about POC, if going there will prevent you staying in a stance of non-judgment.

THE KEY STEPS WITHIN THE ASK PHASE

1. Once you hear a racially-problematic statement, you should assess how suitable the setting is to engage in some dialogue, let it go, or make a "rejoinder" that expresses disagreement but is not really an invitation to more dialogue. (In the Odds and Ends section at the end of the workbook, there is a Ladder of Retorts with options for different ways to respond to racially-problematic statements.) As you make this assessment, you should consider issues such as time, level of privacy, atmosphere, your and the skeptic's moods, your relationship with the skeptic, and so on.
2. Think about how deeply you want to pursue their views about race, and their feelings toward people of color.

10 I listened to my Jewish father talk about the schvartze, and how they were going to try to come in and steal everything. So I grew up with a lot of narratives. I recently had a black family move into my neighborhood. And even thought I staunchly want to be an ally, all of these things come up. "There goes the neighborhood. The property values are going to go down. Dammit those people are loud. They talk 10 times louder than white people What's up with them? The dogs are barking all day long…don't they ever train their dogs? Why don't they fix the muffler on their car?" So the point is if you want to be an ally, I think that you have to admit that you have those voices and you have to give other people the permission to have those voices. I think the important work is that we identify our own unconscious bias. – Participant in White Ally Toolkit Workshop, Pittsfield MA

3. Ask questions to learn more about their beliefs about race/racism. Pay attention to how skeptical they are that racism matters in the situation you are talking about. If you decide to go deeper, you might also ask questions about their beliefs about people of color that they might feel uncomfortable expressing.
4. Don't focus the conversation too long on their beliefs. Instead, inquire about an experience or two that they think validates their beliefs.
5. Make a strong effort to let them know you are not judging them for their beliefs, even if you may feel very differently. If you are judging them, try to hide it. Let them know that you find their experiences interesting to hear about.

PHASE 3: CONNECT

EVEN THOUGH YOU SEE RACIAL ISSUES RATHER DIFFERENTLY FROM THEM, SHARE AN ANECDOTE OR TWO LIKELY TO HAVE SOME RESONANCE WITH THEM THAT IS RELEVANT TO THE TOPIC.

Your primary goal in this phase is to demonstrate to the skeptic that you have some level of alignment with them. As noted above, most racism-minimizing views encompass some belief about reality that is actually true. However, many racism skeptics have been taught to think of these beliefs as antithetical to the idea that racism against POC is a real problem. Thus, for many skeptics - especially ideologically conservative ones - their perspectives about race are part of a larger battle between what they see as healthy conservative values (hard work, obeying authority, merit, and uniform standards, to name a few) and the liberal attack on these values. In this phase of the dialogue, your goal is to offer a story or two that make it harder for them to see you as the enemy of these values, because you are connecting with them on some piece of their viewpoint.

If their racism-denying point of view is something that you used to believe, you can potentially create a moment of connection even stronger than when you have to find one truth embedded in their viewpoint. If at some point in your past, you held the view they have now, your best bet may be to let them know that. You can just say that, but often it is more powerful to convey a brief anecdote. This may as simple as recounting a conversation that happened long ago. The key is to tell the story in a way that does not convey judgment of yourself in the past, which means that you are not judging them now.

THE KEY STEPS WITHIN THE CONNECT PHASE

1. Share a brief story or two that aligns with as much of the skeptic's views as you authentically can.
2. If you have ever thought like they did, describe an experience that illustrates your thinking this way. Do not frame your prior perspective as "stupid" or "unenlightened." Remember, you are not saying everything they believe about race is true. Rather, for a brief moment, you are telling them that you agree with a small piece of what they believe, or that you used to think like they do.
3. If you have external data or facts that validate the part of the issue you agree on, share this information. (For instance, if you are dealing with the statement "No one is racist anymore," it may be helpful to state your knowledge of national opinion survey data showing how much racial bigotry has declined in the past 50 years).[11]
4. If it will not be perceived as weird, create a moment – even if it is very brief eye contact - where you and the skeptic are taking in the fact that you do have some agreement on an aspect of the issue.

This last point is largely the door to the rest of the conversation. It is important to make the skeptic feel that you place some importance on the point of agreement. In most instances, this can happen non-verbally, perhaps with a brief pause and direct eye contact. Your intention is to create a brief moment where you are sharing in the sense of alignment. Remember, you are about to invite them to expand their thinking. No matter how gently you do this, they may experience this as telling them their prior thinking has been wrong. It is important that they know you feel that they have been right about something.

11 For example, in the proportion of whites who oppose laws prohibiting inter-racial

I listened to my Jewish father talk about the schvartze, and how they were going to try to come in and steal everything. So I grew up with a lot of narratives. I recently had a black family move into my neighborhood. And even thought I staunchly want to be an ally, all of these things come up. "There goes the neighborhood. The property values are going to go down. Dammit those people are loud. They talk 10 times louder than white people What's up with them? The dogs are barking all day long...don't they ever training their dogs? Why don't they fix the muffler on their car?" So the point is if you want to be an ally, I think that you have to admit that you have those voices and you have to give other people the permission to have those voices. I think the important work is that we identify our own unconscious bias.

Participant in White Ally Toolkit Workshop, Pittsfield MA

---

marriage was less than 38% in 1963, and is more than about 90% now. Similarly, the proportion of whites who thought that blacks and whites should attend the same schools was about 50% in 1955, and is about 95% now. Citation: http://igpa.uillinois.edu/programs/racial-attitudes

PHASE 4: EXPAND

RELATE YOUR EXPERIENCES THAT SUGGEST A BROADER UNDERSTANDING OF RACE/RACISM THAN THEY HAVE NOW

By this point, you have established that each of you have had personal experiences with legitimate sources of truth, wisdom, and insight. You have also established that you are not some raving liberal apologist who enables the dysfunctional behavior of POC, but rather that you actually agree with at least some specific element of how they view the situation. The next step is to share one or two stories that illustrate the larger truth about race and racism that you see. Ideally, these should be first-person experiences. A less preferred but still useful option is to recount a second-hand experience that might have affected you deeply when you first heard it. Your objective is to help the skeptic see that if the same experiences had happened to them, they might have come to a similarly expanded understanding of how racism works.

It is best if you have at least two stories in your arsenal. If you told a "I used to think like that" story (i.e. an "I confess"), it will be useful to not only relate an experience linked to your "waking up", but also one that shows that you still have experiences that confirm your new view. If your Connect story focused on one embedded truth within their overall perspective (i.e. an "I concur"), it will still be helpful if you have additional ones that animates your view that race/racism matters. A skeptic may try to frame your first story as anomalous or invalid for some other reason.

THE KEY STEPS WITHIN THE EXPAND PHASE

1. Assess which personal experiences you have had that are most suitable, given the topic, setting, and dispositions of the skeptic. Decide whether to use the longer or shorter version of the stories, given the setting, your level of connection with the skeptic, their apparent ability to listen, and similar factors.
2. Tell your anecdote(s), while noting how much the skeptic is engaged.

3. If the skeptic wants to argue with your conclusions, it may be necessary to gently remind them that you are not trying to make them believe anything. Instead you are simply sharing experiences thatled you to see things not seen before.
4. If you think it has a reasonable chance of success, ask the skeptic whether they have ever had an experience that supports your perspective. Such a question might look like:
    - » Have you ever seen a time when a cop gave a white person a big break when they did not have to?
    - » Even if you don't feel this all of the time, have you ever felt grateful that you were not a person of color given how many of them seem to constantly wonder how they will be received?
    - » Has there been a time in the last 10 years when a white person surprised you with how unabashed they were about their dislike of an entire racial/ethnic group?

Note: the strategy of asking a skeptic for experiences that align with your view should be used only when you sense they have has actually joined you in an open-minded inquiry into the issue. It is easy for this strategy to activate either your or the skeptic's argumentative impulses, which is not helpful to your goal of a joint dialogic inquiry into the topic.

EXPAND – EXTENSION 1
EXPLORE THE SEEMING CONTRADICTIONS

In many circumstances, it is useful to take a break from the storytelling and lift up a question that expands the view of a situation. This is useful for people who are conceptual thinkers or who have a bent toward curiosity. The purpose of this step, if you take it, is to get their agreement that your conversation may be uncovering an additional truth that is not completely at odds with what you have already agreed on. One of the most direct expressions of this is in the form of: Can X be true, AND also Y also be true? Here are some examples of what a question like this might look like:

- Is it possible that the vast majority of police are fair AND a significant minority treat POC differently some of the time?
- Could it be that many poor people of color make bad choices AND there are fewer opportunities available for them than for white people?
- Is it possible that people can have no conscious negative views of other groups AND still have biases against them that they are not aware of?

By expanding the conversation in this way, you are signaling that you are not trying to refute their position, particularly the part you agreed to. Rather, you are trying to add a new truth that acknowledges racism, to the collective understanding of truth that you and the skeptic share. Sometimes, raising these conceptual questions can get their buy-in for more dialogue and future exploration of the topic.

This strategy of exploring the seeming contradictions can be used before telling your Expand story--or after, to “put a bow on” the racial dialogue conversation you have just had. In each of the modules on specific topics, we provide some questions that might expand the conversation.

THE KEY STEPS WITHIN EXPAND EXTENSION 1

1. Make a decision about whether this is a situation where raising a broader view question is more likely to enhance or derail the momentum of the conversation.
2. Think about which specific question is most appropriate, given what you have already shared and which stories you might bring to bear next.
3. Raise the question, and try (not too hard) to get them to assert that it is a somewhat interesting question.

EXPAND – EXTENSION 2
HIGHLIGHT DATA, FACTS, OR ILLUSTRATIONS THAT SUPPORT A BROADER VIEW

If the skeptic has joined you with a spirit of some curiosity about you conversation, you may choose to go beyond direct experience as a way of furthering your point that racism against POC is a thing. This is when you can bring into the conversation facts, data, research findings, and other similar information.

Our hope is that white allies prepare for such moments, and have practiced relating a fact that powerfully drives home a specific aspect of racism. It would be great if you have many facts to choose from. But it is vital that the skeptic feels that you are not trying to beat them into submission with facts. Many people who are skeptical of racism are defending a position they have deep emotional attachments to. If you are clearly attempting to blow them away with overwhelming evidence, the Backfire Effect might only become stronger and roll back the progress you made.

A few points to keep in mind:

- Skeptics will more likely accept your facts if you have earlier brought up facts that support some part of their point of view.
- Polling data often can make compelling points to skeptics who are open to science.
- Large scale social science experiments (e.g. sending out hundreds of resumes to employers and testing whether "ethnic sounding" names get a difference response from "white sounding" names) can sometimes make powerful points.

THE KEY STEPS WITHIN EXPAND EXTENSION 2

1. Take a mental note of facts (or findings, analogies, etc.) that you can easily and comfortably relay that seem relevant to the conversation.
2. Choose 2-3 that best support your attempt to broaden the skeptic's view.

3. Float one fact, and note how effective it seemed in keeping the skeptic's mind open.
4. If deploying a fact is useful, bring another to bear when the time seems appropriate.

Note: Though allies often find them compelling, be cautious in using analogies, metaphors, allegories, and conceptualizations. Sometimes, these rhetorical strategies are extremely useful in helping novice allies think in a new way about race. On the other hand, you need to carefully think through whether rhetorical strategies that are in fact helpful when engaging racism skeptics. As helpful as the right metaphor or example can be to illuminate the complexities of race and racism for some allies, they are only powerful if the listener already believes that racism is real.

CLOSE THE CONVERSATION

It is important not to stay in this conversation to the point of diminishing returns. Remember, you are not likely to change someone's perspective about racism in one sitting – though of course this happens now and then. Most likely, you will need to engage them in multiple conversations to shift deeply ingrained views.

A critical point to remember is that a skeptic will have more difficulty getting out of denial about racism if they sense that you are trying to change their entire ideological worldview. You should only try to influence the current conversation. (This will be discussed a bit more in Odds and Ends.)

Your goal is not to get them to admit defeat to your superior logic; instead, you are trying to get them to be honestly intrigued by the possibility that the world is somewhat more complex than they had previously thought.

Even on the specific topic you are discussing, your goal is not to get them to admit defeat to your superior logic; instead, you are trying to get them to be honestly intrigued by the possibility that the world is somewhat more complex than they had previously thought.

Doing that may mean articulating a question that positions your conversation as a joint attempt to make sense of things. A straightforward one is: "Given everything we have said, how do you think that we should try to make sense of all of this?" Whether or not you raise a question that intrigues the skeptic, you should consider whether you want to get them to have additional conversations with you.

These steps may be helpful as you try to close the conversation

1. Assess whether the skeptic would likely find a thought-provoking question to be the best way to end the conversation. If so, ask it as you attempt to wrap up the conversation.
2. No matter how you transition away from the conversation, convey your appreciation to the person for being willing to share their experiences, and for listening to your experiences.
3. Remember, you are not trying to claim a victory; you are also not trying to transform their entire worldview and ideology.
4. Tell them that you would like to talk again. If you can say so sincerely, tell them you don't have conversations like this as often as you would like to, that you have enjoyed it, and you hope they did too.
5. Unless doing so would seem weird, make some actual plan to talk again.

DEBRIEFING YOUR ENGAGEMENT

Having covered this much ground with the skeptic, it is useful to do some reflection on which tactics seemed to increase the skeptic's engagement, and which did not. You might do this in writing. Hopefully, you are connected with other allies who are also trying to improve their engagement of racism skeptics; if so, having a conversation with them might be helpful.

Some questions that you should consider as part of your debriefing:

1. Were there moments when your listening skills were better or worse than others? What lessons can you draw about how you can be a more effective listener?

____

____

____

____

2. Which point of agreement did you focus on in your Connect stories? How effective was your storytelling in creating the feeling of alignment? Might a different point of agreement have produced a different outcome?

3. How did your attempt to expand the skeptic's view go? What stories did you tell? Is there something that you might have done differently to be more effective?

4. Were there any subtle moves in the exchange, outside of the storytelling, that seemed to increase or decrease the skeptic's engagement?

The rest of this part of the workbook focuses on applying the RACE Method to specific racism-denying sentiments that skeptics often express.

STRUCTURE OF THE MODULES

What follows are eight modules that provide guidance about applying the RACE Method to specific sentiments that racism skeptics express. The modules provide a clear but flexible plan for how to manage the dialogue journey, which will probably last more than one conversation. Each includes sample questions that you might raise with the skeptic, as well as reflection questions to construct first- or second-hand brief anecdotes that you can use in the conversation. For the most part, each module follows the sequence of steps outlined in the RACE Method.

The goal of the modules is to give you an engagement strategy for addressing a troubling statement – in the moment or later - instead of labeling the person as "racist" or "racially backward" and either attacking them or doing nothing.

The eight sentiments included the Spring 2018 edition of the workbook are:

1. "Racism means having intentionally negative views of other groups. I am colorblind. So if I don't have conscious negative intent, I don't have to worry about being racist."
2. "Nowadays, there are very few advantages to being white. I am not privileged."
3. "The economic problems of people of color are primarily due to the bad choices that they make."
4. "Slavery and segregation were a long time ago. We should not talk about them anymore and just move on."
5. "If people of color would just act properly, law enforcement would treat them fairly."
6. "Very few people are consciously racist anymore."

7. "It is vital that America drastically reduce the level immigration so that we can return to our cultural greatness."
8. "Those athletes and others protesting should be grateful they live in America and should not disrespect the nation and the flag by kneeling during the National Anthem. "

The modules follow a similar format, which is reviewed and explained below.

ALTERNATE ARTICULATIONS

For many of the modules, you will see alternative ways that this sentiment gets expressed. Your objective is not to listen for the exact words, but rather for the core sentiment. (Most allies will recognize them - because of their visceral reaction.) When these ideas are expressed, you should make a decision about whether this moment has the potential of being a good starting place for a dialogue journey with the skeptic. If this is not the best moment, you might say you will get back to them later. Then you can refer to the relevant module, and prepare for the next time you will talk to them.

For some statements, there is an overview that conveys some relevant guidelines about the way that skeptics tend to view this issue. This information is meant to give you broad thematic guidance about your strategy for engaging the issue. In some cases, this discussion will focus on ideas that allies often spend energy fighting skeptics about unnecessarily; it is important to not let the conversation energy exhaust itself while pursuing the wrong goal. In some cases, this will include the most likely elements of Connect and Expand anecdotes.

PHASE 1: REFLECT

As discussed in Part One, it is important to reflect on what kind of statements are "hot buttons" for you and are likely to impede your attentive and empathetic listening. (Hot buttons are issues that, when raised, throw you enough off center that you are subject to making flawed moment-to-moment decisions.) You should also reflect on what strategies you should take to recover if you are thrown off balance. Some topics are more likely to cause you emotional upset than others. As was discussed in Part One, it is vital to reflect on your listening challenges, and remind yourself of strategies to stay in empathetic mode when skeptics say things that are hard to hear. Some allies have found that each racism-denying sentiment has specific hot buttons that are likely to emerge in conversation. Reflect on whether each of these issues reveals emotional landmines for you. Having said that, the Reflect description in the modules that follow assume you will do the appropriate amount of reflection on these issues for each topic.

The module will proceed by providing reflection questions for four types of anecdotes to consider for each racially-problematic statement.

CONNECT ANECDOTE TYPE 1

These are anecdotes in which you identify some embedded element of the speaker's perspective that you find to have merit. Each module will provide some questions to get you to reflect on potentially meritorious ideas embedded within a skeptic's overall racism-minimizing perspective. The hope is that you can find an anecdote that conveys your alignment with a true idea buried within the skeptic's point of view. We will refer to this as the "I exactly half agree with you" or an "I concur" story. (Some allies have found this phrase to be an intriguing way of signifying partial agreement with somebody at the beginning of a conversation.)

CONNECT ANECDOTE TYPE 2

These are anecdotes to convey that you understand much of the skeptic's overall perspective because you used to think that way yourself. This will only apply in some cases, because many allies never looked at the issue that way. But when an ally can authentically convey that they have empathy for a skeptic because they used to think that way themselves, the conversation often can make significant progress. If you can non-judgmentally look back at your own previous perspective – and thus at the skeptic's current view – you can enhance the sense of emotional connection with the person. Perhaps more importantly, you can also present your current perspective as one that is merely enhanced by more information and experience. Depicting your subsequent racism-acknowledging position in this way can help the skeptic see that they are not bending to your will, but rather going down a developmental path based on learning new information. We will refer to this anecdote as the "I used to think that way" story or an "I confess" story.

EXPAND ANECDOTE TYPE 1

These anecdotes are the flip side of the "I used to think that way" stories. Ideally these stories vividly capture some experience that was part of your becoming more "woke" to some aspect of the issue being discussed – usually, this is a reality that is based on seeing issues of race and racism that were previously invisible to you. It is best if this anecdote can be highlighted in a specific personal story that has a powerful moment when your new understanding came together. In reality, sometimes white allies' new understandings are baked over a period of time through many experiences - in a class, conversations with people, or by consuming media. You are not encouraged to lie about your experience. However, most people will be more impacted by the story of a specific moment when a new realization came together powerfully, even if that moment was preceded by reading, a class, several conversations, or some set of gradually accumulating experiences. The reflection questions for this type of anecdote try to get you to recall an experience when your new understanding came to a head. We will refer to this as your "But later, I realized" story.

EXPAND ANECDOTE TYPE 2

These anecdotes are ones that you might share to make the point that you have had experiences that validate your view of the issue at hand. If you had a "But later, I realized", this anecdote will likely have occurred later than that. You will relate these anecdotes to convey personal experiences that support your view of the issue rather than theirs. The reflection questions are designed to help you think through your experiences in the hopes that you can find anecdotes that are clear, compelling, and persuasive to most people. We will refer to these as "Why I see it this way" stories.

The reflection questions are presented in clusters by their type. There is space to take notes that seem most compelling, and perhaps to start constructing your anecdotes.

PHASE 2: ASK

As discussed, your goal in this critical phase is to get the skeptic to discuss some experiences that animate their point of view. The module will provide questions that have a good chance of being fruitful, given the patterns in how racism skeptics think about these issues. This section of each module includes initial questions that help you probe their beliefs beyond what they initially said.

Each module includes space for additional questions that might be useful.

PHASE 3: CONNECT

After you have attentively listened to the skeptic convey an experience or two that lies beneath their belief, you want to turn the conversation to anecdotes that will help you connect with them. In the Connect section, jot down the core elements of the anecdotes you plan to use, based on the Reflect questions that have been provided. To assist your thinking about and telling the anecdote, the module provides space for you to jot down the set-up, the key moment, and the take-away from the anecdote. Having clarity about these points will be helpful in order for you to tell your anecdote compellingly and in multiple lengths as the circumstance warrants.

PHASE 4: EXPAND

After you have solidified your connection with the skeptic through sharing anecdotes, the RACE Method suggests you shift the conversation to stories that embody your perspective that race/racism does matter, to a reasonable understanding of the topic. The module will highlight key possible takeaways from your anecdote, and provide space to jot down the core elements of the story.

In some modules (e.g. Patriotism, Slavery/Jim Crow), it is suggested that you take the skeptic through a multi-staged back and forth. This will be briefly reviewed in the Overview Notes and more extensively addressed in the Expand explanation.

EXPAND – EXTENSION 1: EXPLORE THE SEEMING CONTRADICTION

Many racism skeptics look at race-related issues in a defensive way; they are subject to thinking that the existence of racism potentially obliterates everything they understand about how people and institutions work. As mentioned in Part One, your position is not that racism is the dominant factor in every interaction, but rather that racism often matters to what happens in interactions. The objective of the RACE Method is to use the sharing of experiences to convey the message that you don't think the skeptic's view of the world is completely wrong, but rather that you have come to learn about an additional factor (race/racism) that helps explain situations more fully.

For some people, you can explicitly articulate these factors at a conceptual level. You may find that it is helpful to remind them that the idea that racism sometimes matters does not destroy their conception of the world. For example, it is possible that most police officers are good AND that unconscious racial bias too frequently affects how POC are treated. In some cases, you may float the possibility that something the skeptic typically views as the exact opposite of racism may not, in fact, be contradicted by the existence of racism. Posing this question, just after you have provided experiential evidence, is sometimes powerful in opening people's minds to the idea that racism sometimes matters.

To move the skeptic forward, each module includes a table that frames some beliefs as potentially co-existing with racism-acknowledging beliefs. For some people, articulating things this way will be helpful; for others, doing so may be counter-productive. The hope is that you will experiment with such articulations, and pay attention to lessons you learn about when such articulations are helpful and when they are not.

At the end of some modules are a few additional notes that you may find helpful.

COMBATING RACISM DENIAL: THE MODULES

RACISM-DENYING STATEMENT MODULE 1: RACISM MEANS HAVING INTENTIONAL LY NEGATIVE VIEWS OF OTHER GROUPS. SO IF I DON'T HAVE CONSCIOUS NEGATIVE INTENT, I DON'T HAVE TO WORRY ABOUT BEING RACIST.

ALTERNATE VERSIONS

- "I have a lot of friends of color, so I can't be racist."
- "I am colorblind."
- "Racist applies to people like the KKK. "
- "All of this talk of unconscious racism is really aimed at making white people feel guilty for something they did not do."

POTENTIAL KEY POINTS FOR YOUR CONNECT STORIES

1. Intentions are important, and not having negative intentions is an important thing to recognize.
2. Given that many people were exposed to negative messages about POC, white people who have resisted consciously embracing these messages should be acknowledged for this.
3. Many people were taught to be colorblind by adults; this teaching has some value at some points in childhood.
4. There has been progress over the decades with fewer white people having hostile feelings about people of color.
5. Sometimes, assertions that white people are racist are inaccurate. On occasions, these assertions are made cynically.

POTENTIAL KEY POINTS FOR YOUR EXPAND STORIES

1. Most white people were exposed to negative messages about POC. Many - perhaps most – absorbed these messages at least a little. Doing so does not make you a bad person.
2. It is possible to absorb these messages in ways that are below your conscious awareness. That is, unconscious racism is a real thing.
3. Sometimes, good-hearted white people mentally turn people of color into "other groups", and this can happen consciously, semi-consciously, or unconsciously.
4. It is healthy to admit that these messages have affected you, and we should not shame ourselves or others for doing so. (There will be more discussion of shame in Odds and Ends). In fact, admitting these messages exist is key to reducing their effect on us.
5. It is possible to believe that one is colorblind and still unconsciously think of people in some racial groups as other.
6. Even though the teaching to be colorblind can have value at some point, it can also lead people to not recognize some important ways that human perceptions actually function.

Note: This module will prompt you to try to formulate three Connect and three Expand stories. The concept of othering/unconscious bias is one of the most important in modern race relations, so it is suggested that you put extra effort into creating engagement strategies about this topic.

PHASE 1: REFLECT

Reflection Questions for "I exactly half agree with you" Anecdotes

1. Describe an experience where you realized there was a difference between two white people in their level of bad intentions toward people of color. It is OK if one of the persons is you.
2. As you were growing up, did you ever resist the message that you should harbor negative feelings against a different racial group?
3. If you have ever observed an incident where a white person was accused of having bad intentions against a person of color and you

thought this was unfair, jot some notes about it.

4. If you were taught to be colorblind by your parents and you tried to follow this teaching, make a few notes about what you were taught and how you tried to follow it.
5. When it came down to open discussions about race in your family and friendship circles, how was this issue discussed?
6. When did you first notice that you were receiving messages that encouraged you to see some people of color as other? (These messages may have come from family, friends, the media, or other sources). What were some of these messages?
7. How did you feel about these messages at the time? Did you ever feel: a sense of pride in your group? Relief that you were not in another group? Pity for other groups? Angry at the messengers?
8. If you have recent examples of a person of color having an unconscious bias against a white person, make some notes about it here.

Reflection Questions for "I used to feel that way" Anecdotes

1. If you can remember having resistance to the idea of unconscious bias before you grew in your acceptance of it, make a few notes that will allow you to capture your previous sense of disbelief.
2. Within your family circles, how was the idea of othering or unconscious bias discussed? Within your friendship circles?

Reflection Questions for "But later, I realized" Anecdotes

1. What was a formative experience that taught you that unconscious bias matters, outside the context of race?
2. What was a formative experience that taught you that unconscious racial bias matters?
3. Can you remember an early experience where you noticed that you had an unconscious bias against a group? How did you learn this? How did you feel? Was there a part of you that wanted to reject the idea that this was possible? Do you remember a time when this happened because of race?

4. Can you remember an early time when you mentally turned people from a different group (maybe not race-based) into “other”?

Reflection Questions for “Why I see it this way” Anecdotes

1. Do you have any recent stories that powerfully illustrate someone having unconscious bias against a POC?
2. Do you have any stories within the past 10 years that illustrate another white person looking at a POC as other even if only for a moment?
3. Have you ever noticed yourself mentally turning a POC into an other?
4. Do you ever have reactions to people in other racial groups that you don’t like to admit to yourself?
5. Have you ever noticed yourself having an emotional reaction to POC that differs from how you feel about similar white people? Feeling more afraid of POC, for example? More superior?
6. Have you ever noticed yourself acting differently towards POC than you do towards white people?
7. Have you ever come to the conclusion that the narrative of “I am colorblind” actually can be harmful to your or other people’s self-awareness?
8. Have you ever noticed a situation where a white person appeared to see a person of color as other but had little awareness of this?

PHASE 2: ASK QUESTIONS THAT DRAW OUT THE SKEPTIC’S PERSPECTIVE AND THE EXPERIENCES BEHIND IT.

Potentially useful experience questions to ask your skeptic

1. What were you taught about race and bias growing up? Were you taught to be colorblind, and if so, how much did this teaching help and/or hurt you? Were there any differences in the views of the adults who were in a position to influence you?
2. Did you ever consciously attempt to ensure that you had no biases against any group? Why did you do this?
3. When it came down to your family and friendship circles, how were these issues discussed?

4. Have you ever seen a white person unfairly accused of having a bias against a person of color?
5. What do you think about the idea of unconscious bias? What is an experience that helped solidify your point of view about this?

PHASE 3: SHARE AN EXPERIENCE THAT CONNECTS TO THE SKEPTIC'S PERSPECTIVE

Use the following space to clarify the anecdotes that you will tell to connect to a piece of the skeptic's view.

Connect Anecdote One

Describe the situation:

____

____

Describe the key moment that illustrates the takeaway that connects to the skeptic's view:

____

____

Clarify the takeaway:

____

____

Connect Anecdote Two

Describe the situation:

____

____

Describe the key moment that illustrates the takeaway that connects to the skeptic's view:

____

____

Clarify the takeaway:

____

____

Connect Anecdote Three

Describe the situation:

____

____

Describe the key moment that illustrates the takeaway that connects to the skeptic's view:

____

____

Clarify the takeaway:

____

____

Note: One potential concern of racism skeptics is that the idea of unconscious bias will produce a level of self-doubt that is irritating. This has some truth of course – if you know about the possibility of unconscious bias and you are committed to treating people equally, there is more for you to think about. If the skeptic raises this concern, it is valuable to not initially rebut this observation. Later in the conversation, you can come back to the idea that this additional complexity is worth the trouble because of your commitment to treating everyone with the respect they deserve.

PHASE 4: EXPAND

An option before you tell your Expand anecdote(s):
You will need to make a decision about whether it is useful to probe them about if and when they have experienced bias because of some characteristic that is not about race. Recognizing an experience they have had of non-racial bias may help them overcome their resistance to the idea of racial bias. The question might be phrased something like this:

Leaving race aside, have you ever been in a situation where you felt that someone's behavior toward you was biased because of who you were, and they were not even aware of it?

Many thoughtful people will have at least one example, because bias is such a pervasive phenomenon. If they have an answer, you might ask a follow up probe about whether there were others who observed this situation who did not think bias was occurring. The purpose of this follow up is to establish that even in cases where the target is confident bias is at work, both the perpetrator and some bystanders to the situation might disagree.

Put your notes about the Expand anecdotes below.

Expand Anecdote One

Describe the situation:

____

____

Describe the key moment that illustrates the takeaway that might expand the skeptic's view:

____

____

Clarify the takeaway:

Expand Anecdote Two

Describe the situation:

Describe the key moment that illustrates the takeaway that might expand the skeptic's view:

Clarify the takeaway:

Expand Anecdote Three

Describe the situation:

Describe the key moment that illustrates the takeaway that might expand the skeptic's view:

Clarify the takeaway:

____

____

Make sure you manage the time and energy in this conversation so that it does not run out of steam. Your primary goal is to shift from the Connect to an anecdote to establish that you – a good-hearted white person – has been someone who has acted on an unconscious bias.

For this issue, it can be especially useful to have one story in which you concluded that you were operating based on a bias, and one in which you notice another white person's bias affecting their response to a POC. If the white person did not notice this until it was pointed out to them and later realized it, so much the better.

It is useful to have a couple of stories about unconscious bias that do not involve you. Many skeptics believe that whites who think racism is real have been duped by a progressive rhetorical regime that blames guilty white liberals for all of the self-inflicted problems of POC. Stories that depict unconscious bias being recognized by other whites helps to counter that idea. In the best-case scenario, the skeptic will get the message that bias is not only recognized by you and other white people, but also that even unintended bias can have a big impact.

If you have one or more of these stories, try to enliven the POC in the story. Your overall message is that unconscious bias is a relatively small and easy to commit offense by well-meaning white people, but that it can result in significant impacts on POC.

You will need to make a decision about whether/how to broach if they have ever operated on a bias. They may naturally bring this up. But many skeptics will not do so because this topic can be emotionally disturbing. This sequence of the conversation has suggested to them that they might be a "racist", and this may feel very scary. It may be important to let the conversation settle so they can integrate all that they have learned.

Hopefully, this is not the last conversation you will have with them.

OPTIONAL STEP: EXPLORE THE SEEMING CONTRADICTIONS

As mentioned, you may decide to put a bow on the conversation by exploring the seeming contradictions would be helpful to your objectives. If so, the following table can be supportive.

Perhaps it is true that	*AND*	it is also true that
Having positive intentions toward other groups is critically important	**and**	There are still some people who have both positive intentions and biases about other groups they are not aware of
Sometimes people are accused of being unconsciously bias and this may not be true	**and**	Sometimes people act on biases they don't see until later
Considering unconscious bias makes it more complicated to get through situations	**and**	Connecting to this hidden factor makes our lives fairer, richer, and more interesting

FINAL NOTES

There is a wealth of scientific studies and objective data showing that unconscious bias against POC is widespread. There is a great deal of similarly objective data that shows that the subtle bias of whites has a profound impact on the lives of POC.

If you find yourself in conversations about unconscious bias more than a few times, it might be useful to familiarize yourself with both of these types of data. It will be important to make good choices about when and how to deploy this information. Skeptics vary in how they respond to data of this type. Some have a higher degree of something called "scientific curiosity", which means they are more open to being persuaded by evidence that might disconfirm their original point of view. On the other hand, there are those who become more hardened in their position when confronted with data that suggests they are wrong. So think about whether and how to move to a data-based conversation with the skeptic you are talking to.

Discussing Internalized Racism May Be Useful

There is an important fact related to unconscious bias that may help you even with skeptics who are not oriented toward hard data. **Specifically, many POC have a negative bias against their own group.** This fact has been borne out by the results of the Implicit Association Test that has been taken by millions of people.

As an illustration, Pew Research found that about 28% of African-Americans who take this instrument demonstrate an implicit preference for whites over African-Americans (48% of whites do this, according to the same poll).[12] Part Three of this workbook has a sub-section on Unconscious Bias/Othering with references that may get you started in finding helpful external sources.

Since many skeptics associate racial bias with bigotry that they find morally reprehensible, you can position the facts about internalized racism by POC to show that racism is not a personal moral failing by individual whites, but rather is a societal problem affecting everyone.

12 http://www.pewsocialtrends.org/2015/08/19/exploring-racial-bias-among-biracial-and-single-race-adults-the-iat/

Another piece of data that gives skeptics a certain degree of cover to posit or admit the possibility of bias comes from a comment by Jesse Jackson. "There is nothing more painful to me at this stage in my life than to walk down the street and hear footsteps and start thinking about robbery. Then look around and see somebody white and feel relieved.... After all we have been through. Just to think we can't walk down our own streets, how humiliating."[13]

The following quote by Marlene Watson along the same lines may be useful at the right moment:

> "What is the black shadow? It's the running inner dialogue we have with ourselves all day long about our fears of being inferior as black people. It is our internalization of the white man's lie that blacks are inferior to whites -- the very lie that was the foundation of our ancestors' enslavement."[14]

On Language

Depending on their level of skepticism to racially progressive rhetoric, it may be counter-productive to label this behavior "racist" in your first conversation. In progressive circles, saying "I too, am racist," can do some important tone setting for collective explorations of a group's complicity in a society that exhibits racism. But remember, many skeptics are in a deep ideological battle with what they see as excessively race-conscious rhetoric coming from the progressive movement. Think through whether the understanding of the skeptic is best served by such confessional language, or whether you are better off framing biases that you have demonstrated in a more low-key way. Calling this feeling "racial prejudice" instead might be helpful, for example.

Don't let the conversation become distracted by an argument about terms. Whether they call it "racism", "racial prejudice", "bias" or other terms

13 Remarks at a meeting of Operation PUSH in Chicago (27 November 1993). Quoted in "Crime: New Frontier - Jesse Jackson Calls It Top Civil-Rights Issue" by Mary A. Johnson, 29 November 1993, Chicago Sun-Times (ellipsis in original). Partially quoted by Bob Herbert, 12 December 1993, New York Times.

14 From Facing the Black Shadow, Marlene F. Watson, 2013.

is much less important than getting the skeptic to acknowledge that sometimes people are affected by such thoughts without being aware of it.

Do Not Ask For a Concession Speech

Remember, at one or more points in your conversational journey, check how the skeptic is integrating their experiences, the experiences you have shared, as well as whatever data you have brought to bear. This may be as simple as asking something like, "What do you make of all of this that we have talked about?" Your goal is not get them to make a summary concession to you. If you get the skeptic to consider that this conversation has been thought provoking and they want to come back to it, you can declare victory mentally, and celebrate the success later with other allies.

RACISM-DENYING STATEMENT MODULE 2: NOWADAYS, THERE ARE VERY FEW ADVANTAGES TO BEING WHITE.

ALTERNATE VERSIONS

- "I have worked for everything I have. The idea that I am privileged is ridiculous."
- "White privilege does not exist."

The core conversational objective is to first acknowledge that white people have struggles. If necessary, you can acknowledge that some POC have an advantage over some white people. Your main message is to convey that it is still easier to be white, though it may not be easy.

POTENTIAL KEY POINTS FOR YOUR CONNECT STORIES

1. Just because you are white does not mean that everything is handed to you easily.
2. There are times when white people – especially ones with working class roots – are looked down upon.
3. The advantages of being white in comparison to POC are less than they used to be. (POC opportunities compared to whites are much better than they used to be.)
4. Even if there are advantages of being white in some circumstances, it may not be helpful to say white people are inherently "racist."
5. Claims of racism/white privilege can be used cynically or in way that tends to silence people.

KEY TAKEAWAY FOR YOUR EXPAND STORIES

You can concede all of the points above because they don't matter to your central point, which is that you have personal experiences that led to your conclusion that being white has advantages.

On Language

> When you are speaking to a white male who has been raised in a white environment, do not bring up the term "white male privilege" and expect them to know what you are talking about. It only goes downhill from there. I realize I had to break it down and get to that point, not start at that point.
>
> White Ally Toolkit Workshop Participant, Long Valley New Jersey

When referring to the cumulative advantages of being white, this project avoids the term "white privilege" because a huge proportion of skeptics have a difficult time seeing themselves as privileged. This term seems to trigger people, and actually worsen the already tough challenge of helping them see that being white has many advantages. The term "white privilege" can become a distraction in a way that other terms do not – such as the mouthful "unearned racial advantage". The anti-racist movement could use more and better alternative language. In the meantime, you need to make a conscious assessment of what terms work, do not work, and when. Hopefully, you will make adjustments as you notice results. It is worth noting that many allies in the workshops have said, unprompted, that the term "white privilege" – while a helpful shortcut when talking to other allies – frequently detracts from the conversation when talking to skeptics.

On Conceptualization

Some skeptics have trouble accepting the asymmetry of white privilege. An advantage of the term "unearned racial advantage" is that it can accommodate the possibility that other groups can benefit from this phenomenon. For instance, black men are assumed to have street smarts, Asian women are assumed to good be in science, and white men are assumed to be trustworthy. In specific circumstances, these stereotypes are helpful. The comparative issue is how often and to what degree do people benefit from unearned racial advantage. If you are at a reasonable level of dialogue with a skeptic, you can have a conversation about this. Given that fair-minded people can usually be led to see the different impacts of unearned racial advantage, you do not have to be afraid of giving ground on which term is used.

PHASE 1: REFLECT ON YOUR OWN PERSONAL STORIES RELATED TO UNEARNED RACIAL ADVANTAGE

Reflection Questions for "I exactly half agree with you" Anecdotes

1. Do you have a sense that there are some white people (e.g. multi-generationally wealthy ones) who look down on white people like you? If so, jot a few notes about an incident that illustrates this disdainful treatment. Include notes on how you felt.
2. Have you ever felt that discussions of white privilege are used to silence white voices on social issues? Have you felt that such discussions contain false assumptions about how easy it is for a white person to find success? Can you think of specific examples where such false thinking was happening, at least in your perceptions at the time?
3. Can you think of a story in which a person of color had some kind of unearned racial advantage?

Reflection Questions for "I used to feel that way" Anecdotes

1. As a child, what were you taught about racial differences? Were you officially taught to be colorblind? Were there other messages that you absorbed about how POC were really better off than whites because of special treatment? Worse off in some ways?
2. Before you became aware of white privilege, what were the strongest arguments that you believed about why you were NOT privileged?
3. What were the experiences that you might have cited to illustrate the idea that white privilege did not exist?
4. Think back to your most memorable initial learnings that race was a real thing in society. Did you ever wonder what it might be like to be a person of color? What did you associate with what it might be like

to be a person of color? Did you imagine that life was easier, or more difficult? In what ways?

Reflection Questions for "But later, I realized" Anecdotes

1. What is your most powerful memory of hearing experiences from a person of color that made it clear to you that white privilege was a real thing?
2. Were there any particularly powerful experiences (yours or someone you trust) that brought home that being white has advantages?

Reflection Questions for "Why I see it this way" Anecdotes

1. What was something that happened to you or family members in the last year that reinforced to you the idea of white privilege?
2. Do you have any second-hand stories from people you trust that convey that being white often entails unearned racial advantages?

PHASE 2: ASK QUESTIONS THAT DRAW OUT THE SKEPTIC'S PERSPECTIVE AND THE EXPERIENCES BEHIND IT

Potential Experience Questions

- Can you think of a time when you felt like the system discriminated against you because you were white?
- Can you think of an experience that illustrates the lack of privilege that you have?
- Has there ever been a time when other white people looked down on you because of some reason that you could not control?
- Describe a time when the idea of white privilege was brought up in a way that really bothered you because you thought it was particularly unfair or self-serving.
- What is something about being white (or about race) that people who focus on white privilege don't or won't understand?

PHASE 3: CONNECT

Which 1-2 stories from your notes are most compelling to demonstrate that you do not completely discount all aspects of the skeptic's views about race and privilege?

Connect Anecdote One

Describe the situation:

___

___

Describe the key moment that illustrates the takeaway that connects to the skeptic's view:

___

___

Clarify the takeaway:

___

___

Connect Anecdote Two

Describe the situation:

___

___

Describe the key moment that illustrates the takeaway that connects to the skeptic's view:

___

___

Clarify the takeaway:

____

____

Connect Anecdote Three

Describe the situation:

____

____

Describe the key moment that illustrates the takeaway that connects to the skeptic's view:

____

____

Clarify the takeaway:

____

____

PHASE 4: EXPAND

In reviewing your experiences related to unearned racial advantage to create an anecdote, the two primary criteria are: 1) you can tell the story powerfully and with some detail if there is time, and 2) almost any reasonable person would agree that the situation involves unearned racial advantage.

With that proviso, it is best to have at least one story that represents an "awakening" in that it relays your transition from questioning white privilege to believing in it. Optimally, you will also have a second story that happened well after you realized that unearned white advantage was real. By deploying these stories at the right time, you can send the message that you have gone along a journey of greater understanding that started where your skeptic is (the earlier Connect story), and that has continued to expand your understanding of how the world works.

Second-hand stories are OK, but usually less effective than those involving you. However, second-hand stories are more effective than academic descriptions or conceptual depictions of the privilege, however powerful they might be. If you use a second-hand story, it is important to not only inhabit it reasonably well, but also have an explanation of why you believe it and trust the person who you heard it from.

Potentially useful stories might include:

- You (or another white person) were given a break for an infraction.
- A POC was treated according to the strict rules, when many white people would have been forgiven or excused.
- You learned that a POC struggled with a greater degree of complexity in a situation because of reasonable concerns that they would be treated more poorly.
- As a member of the dominant group, you had more options in products, historical references, positive images, or other benefits.

Expand Anecdote One

Describe the situation:

____

____

Describe the key moment that illustrates the takeaway that might expand the skeptic's view:

____

____

Clarify the takeaway:

____

____

Expand Anecdote Two

Describe the situation:

____

____

Describe the key moment that illustrates the takeaway that might expand the skeptic's view:

____

____

Clarify the takeaway:

____

____

Expand Anecdote Three

Describe the situation:

____

____

Describe the key moment that illustrates the takeaway that might expand the skeptic's view:

____

____

Clarify the takeaway:

____

____

OPTIONAL STEP: EXPLORE THE SEEMING CONTRADICTIONS

Perhaps it is true that	*AND*	it is also true that
Life can be difficult for the average white person	**and**	Life is somewhat harder for POC because of racism
It is possible for a POC to have more advantages than a white person in some ways	**and**	POC are worse off in some other ways because of racism
Life of POC is much better than it used to be	**and**	There are still advantages of being white today
Many white people can be innocent of racism	**and**	They still benefit from being white
Some of the discourse around white privilege can be distorted	**and**	The concept still might have some validity

FINAL NOTES

At some point, consider the possibility of highlighting data, facts, and illustrations of white racial advantage. Be careful to not become overly focused on gathering them. The following topics related to racial advantage may help refine your thinking and your research.

Ways that institutions treat POC differently, such as discriminatory treatment by:

- Education systems
- Law enforcement
- Health care
- Employers
- Retail sector
- Hospitality sector (e.g. hotels, restaurants)
- Housing and lending

Ways that white people are supported by being in the dominant group, such as :

- Media images that prioritize whiteness (e.g. television, magazines)
- Personal products that cater to whites (e.g. hosiery, Band-Aids, hygiene products)

Ways that white people are more accepted socially, such as within:

- Neighborhoods
- Informal gatherings
- Volunteer organizations

POC coping strategies deal with the uncertainties of how they might be treated:

» Extra measures taken to ease white people's fears
» Extra measures to prove credibility
» "The talk" parents give children about dealing with racism by police or others

There is academic literature and research about all of the aspects of racial privilege mentioned above. You don't need to be an expert on this topic but it is a good idea to have a few facts that build upon your experiences if the dialogue lasts a while. Such information can help make the case that your perceptions about white racial advantage are not aberrant, but are part of a larger pattern.

The Additional Resources section includes references to help learn more about this subject.

Beware of Conversational Touchdown Dances
It is important to remember that your skeptic may be very reluctant to make an adjustment in their thinking about white privilege. Their denial may have marinated for a long time. Don't overplay it and try to force them into submission. If necessary, reassure them that people are not stupid if they don't believe that white privilege is real. The difference between folks who "get" white privilege and those who don't comes down to just having gone through a thought experiment about what it might mean to be someone else. Many astute observers about race have argued that racism is purposefully designed to keep it invisible. In essence, this argument states that part of the way structural racism works is that white people **are supposed to not notice** their unearned racial privileges.

Even while you reassure them that their previous ignorance is nothing to feel bad about, bringing up the purposeful invisibility concept is probably counter-productive -- unless your skeptic is a left-wing progressive who already believes in underlying intellectual structures that tend to reinforce the status quo. If the skeptic is not prone to this type of analysis, do not bring up the "racism is supposed to be invisible" idea; this has a good chance of backfiring. Your best bet is to get them past the white privilege denial, and leave those larger arguments for another day.

RACISM-DENYING STATEMENT MODULE 3: PEOPLE OF COLOR'S ECONOMIC PROBLEMS ARE DUE TO THEIR OWN BAD CHOICES.

ALTERNATE VERSIONS

- "If they just worked harder, people of color would have better lives."
- "If you don't do well in life, you should blame yourself, not racism."
- "When people of color don't do well in life, it's usually because they make bad choices."

Here are some specific beliefs it might be useful to highlight in Connect stories when you are engaging this topic:

1. Putting in hard work is very important to achieving success.
2. There are not enough people who recognize that hard work is important.
3. Even if a person faces difficult circumstances, they can often turn things around through diligent effort.
4. Sometimes, people in a difficult economic situation make decisions that undermine their own success.
5. On occasion, people rely on racism as a reason to not put in sufficient effort to foster their own success.

You can concede all of these points, and may be able to cite an experience that supports these beliefs. At the same time, you also can cite experiences that highlight the idea that POC economic disadvantages are significant and can be difficult for white people to see.

PHASE 1: "REFLECT

Reflection Questions for "I exactly half agree with you" Anecdotes

1. What was a formative experience that taught you the value of hard work when faced with obstacles?
2. Are there people you know/have known whose life stories illustrate the connection between hard work and success? (This might be because they have been diligent and successful or lazy and unsuccessful.)

Reflection Questions for "I used to feel that way" Anecdotes

1. What were you taught (and who taught it) about why POC have created their own situation? Were there opposing voices that you were exposed to?
2. Was there a time in your life when you thought that POC problems were because of their own making?
3. Do you ever find yourself wondering deep down if POC have been deeply damaged by their history, and that this explains their collective lack of economic success? Is there any part of this idea that you might admit to a white skeptic? Does this question cause you to have an emotional reaction?
4. What is your best explanation for why so many POC have much less income and wealth than whites? Do you have competing explanations that you bounce between?

Reflection Questions for "But later, I realized" Anecdotes

Jot some notes about a situation in which you realized that you were experiencing non-obvious advantages or disadvantages that affected success.

1. Have you ever had direct insight into a situation with a POC (or a community) that involved them having significant disadvantages that were not easily apparent? If so, jot some notes about it here.
2. Do you have any experiences that illustrate a white person being conditioned to a lack of opportunity for so long that they learned to expect to fail?
3. What experiences have tended to counter the view that POC create their own economic challenges?
4. What are your best arguments to counter the widespread subtle belief that POC predicament is their own fault? What first- or second-hand experiences do you have that best support these arguments?

PHASE 2: ASK

1. What were you taught growing up about why so many POC are worse off than whites? Were there opposing voices among people you trusted for guidance?

2. Society has always had some amount of talk about the playing field being tilted against POC. What experiences did you have that led you to conclude the playing field is level and groups have the same opportunity?
3. Have you heard explanations of POC economic problems that sounded plausible and those that sounded shaky? (Note: if you use this question, make sure you ask an experience question like #2 to explore beneath their beliefs.)
4. What are questions (or statements) about this issue that you have but don't feel comfortable raising?
5. If you are open to going deeper: Even though people are not supposed to talk about this, surveys show that a fair number think that the reason that folks of color have economic problems is because they are inherently inferior.[15] How do you feel about this point of view? (Note: Be careful to not convey that you assume they think this, only that you are open to talking if that is their actual view.)

PHASE 3: CONNECT

Many racism skeptics believe that people of color and white people who are allied with them use racism as an excuse. Many also believe that POC and white allies don't understand the value of hard work and enable laziness in others. Given this, a primary task is to convey to them that you share their appreciation of the value of diligence in the face of obstacles.

Telling a story that illustrates your deep recognition of the value of hard work does not have to be long and involved. It might be as short as three or four sentences. If the story alludes to others in the same circumstance who did not work as hard, all the better. (It's probably best if they are not POC in case you get a follow up question.) Your core intention is to counter their

15 In a 2016 national study including over 2,000 people, 38% of whites rated blacks as less evolved than whites. This view was held by 52% of Trump supporters. Citation: http://www.slate. com/articles/news_and_politics/politics/2016/11/the_majority_of_trump_supporters_surveyed_described_black_people_as_less.html

suspicion that you are an enabler of POC laziness by asserting that you understand the importance of hard work.

Which 1-2 stories from your notes do you think are most compelling to demonstrate that you do not completely discount all aspects of the skeptic's views about race and economic opportunity?

Connect Anecdote One

Describe the situation:

____

____

Describe the key moment that illustrates the takeaway that connects to the skeptic's view:

____

____

Clarify the takeaway:

____

____

Connect Anecdote Two

Describe the situation:

____

____

Describe the key moment that illustrates the takeaway that connects to the skeptic's view:

____

____

Clarify the takeaway:

____

____

Connect Anecdote Three

Describe the situation:

____

____

Describe the key moment that illustrates the takeaway that connects to the skeptic's view:

____

____

Clarify the takeaway:

____

____

EXPERIENCE QUESTIONS TO ASK A SKEPTIC IF YOU PLAN TO GO DEEPER

Going to More Difficult Territory

As has been mentioned, a sizable proportion (almost 1 of 3) of white Americans are willing to tell an anonymous surveyor they think that some POC (especially blacks) are less hardworking than whites. It would not be shocking if the actual number who held these views is actually higher than that – but many people are likely withholding their feelings even from strangers, because such thoughts are socially unacceptable.

One opportunity for you to deepen your conversations about race is to give room for skeptics to talk honestly about these beliefs. If you want to go to this psychologically risky place, it is important that you make the conversation safe. Doing so may mean that you acknowledging you have been exposed to these ideas yourself, and perhaps absorbed them, at least a little.

The following are some questions to reflect on that can help you construct a productive exchange if you want to go deeper in this way.

1. As a younger person, did any child or adult ever expose you to the idea that POC were lazier or less hardworking than whites? Do you remember your reaction to this?
2. Do you ever find yourself thinking that the reason POC have economic problems is that they just don't work as hard as other people? If so, do you have a counter-narrative, since it is considered socially unacceptable to think that?
3. When you hear the idea from other whites that POC are lazy, what is your reaction, both emotionally and in your behavior? What do you tend to think, feel, and/or say? If you have ever had a conversation with another white person about this, how did it go?
4. How do you feel when you are reminded of the statistic that large proportions of whites are willing to share their beliefs that POC are less hardworking than whites?
5. Have you had experiences that tend to confirm or disconfirm this way of thinking? How do you sort out the experiential evidence about this issue?

To reiterate, it is possible to have a productive exchange about economic opportunity without going to these deeper places. If you choose to do so, you need to be prepared to not judge the skeptic for honestly answering questions that you have taken the initiative to raise.

PHASE 4: EXPAND

Your goal is to tell the anecdote with enough specifics about lessened opportunities for POC so that a reasonable person gets the point. If one of your anecdotes can reinforce the earlier point about how a white person might not see these deficits in opportunity, so much the better. Potentially useful stories might highlight:

- A time when racial discrimination in employment came to light after being initially hidden.
- Your realization that you (or another white person) benefited from a set of positive opportunities in ways that you may have not initially realized.
- How people in minority communities often face a much more limited set of good economic options than white people

Expand Anecdote One

Describe the situation:

____

____

Describe the key moment that illustrates the takeaway that might expand the skeptic's view:

____

____

Clarify the takeaway:

____

____

Expand Anecdote Two

Describe the situation:

____

____

Describe the key moment that illustrates the takeaway that might expand the skeptic's view:

____

____

Clarify the takeaway:

____

____

Expand Anecdote Three

Describe the situation:

____

____

Describe the key moment that illustrates the takeaway that might expand the skeptic's view:

____

____

Clarify the takeaway:

____

____

OPTIONAL STEP: EXPLORE THE SEEMING CONTRADICTIONS

Perhaps it is true that	*AND*	it is also true that
People who are poor often make bad choices that hurt their economic condition.....	**and**	Poor people have much fewer of the opportunities to create success than others?
A variety of conditions have weakened some POCs' attachment to working...	**and**	POCs who have typical levels of industriousness can still face obstacles that most whites do not face
The economic conditions faced by everyone make creating a viable future hard for anyone....	**and**	Issues related to race make it even harder for many POCs in ways that can be hard to see

FINAL NOTES

At the appropriate time, it will be useful to highlight data that illustrates POC are often at a disadvantage with respect to economic opportunity.

Depending on whether the conversation flow still has energy, you may go beyond anecdotes and open up the conversation to data. You will be more effective if you have a few relevant pieces of data in your mental back pocket.

As you look for relevant information, It may be helpful to think about data in a few broad categories:

- Opportunity discrepancies – data that shows that POC have fewer opportunities easily available to them that tend to foster success
- Discrimination - data that shows that even when POC attempt to avail themselves of opportunities, they often face discrimination. Resume experiments and employment-testing experiments can be very powerful.

- Historical/Perceptual - there is historical polling data that shows that even in the early 1960's whites tended to think that POC had equal opportunities available to them.

Whenever you decide to shift the conversation to include data, it is better to start with current rather than historical data. It is likely safer to use historical data about perceptions after marshaling other current facts that they will not have known. Then you can use the historical data to reinforce the point that there have always been dynamics that POC face that white folks did not realize existed.

RACISM-DENYING STATEMENT MODULE 4: SLAVERY AND FORCED SEGREGATION WERE A LONG TIME AGO. WE SHOULD NOT TALK ABOUT THEM ANY MORE AND MOVE ON.

ALTERNATE VERSIONS

- "People bringing up slavery and other problems in the past is just a distraction from the real problems....and sometimes even an excuse."
- "All this talk about historical or institutional racism is a bunch of hooey and a way to keep white people from speaking their minds."

Here are two strategies for advancing the conversation focusing on experiences. Each of them involves highlighting a common dynamic that happens in society, then inviting the skeptic to see how the dynamic can happen in a racial context.

Strategy 1: Explore how each of your lives may be influenced by events that may seem to some people (perhaps yourself when you were younger) to be irrelevant because they happened long ago. Once you establish that sometimes people misperceive how history shapes us, shift the conversation to the racial context.

____

____

____

____

Strategy 2: Explore some common dynamics that happen between people or groups when someone has caused injury or is struggling with healing, and reconciliation may be elusive. After there is some alignment on relevant dynamics, shift the conversation to racial issues.

____

____

PHASE 1: REFLECT

Reflect on your own personal stories related to history and to injury and healing.

Reflection Questions for "I exactly half agree with you" Anecdotes

1. Have you ever seen a situation where a person was legitimately injured emotionally, but took longer to heal from it than you thought was healthy? Have you ever thought someone was nursing an injury to the point where it felt like they were choosing to stay stuck and not move on?
2. Looking back on a situation where you were hurt, have you ever thought that you had nursed the injury longer than you needed?
3. Have you ever seen a situation where a person or a group was injured emotionally, economically or in some other way, and through force of will, put the wound behind them quickly so they could resume their progress?

Reflection Questions for "I used to feel that way" Anecdotes

1. Have you ever thought that a person of color (or POC in general) was too focused on injuries and oppression from the past? Have you ever thought that it was time for them to move on and wondered why they were choosing not to do so? If so, try to recall a moment when you were focused on this issue.
2. Has there been a period in your life when you underestimated the way that decisions made by your parents, grandparents, or others affected your life. If so, how would you describe your view of your life circumstances, before you came to a full understanding?

Reflection Questions for “But later, I realized” Anecdotes

1. Has your life ever been positively or negatively affected by savvy or unfortunate decisions made by previous generations? How did you come to understand the full implications of this? How did you change your narrative about your life after this new understanding?
2. Has anyone in your family ever benefited from institutional practices that operated in a way that excluded non-whites, such as FHA loans before 1975, the GI bill, or restrictive covenants?
3. Have you ever seen a situation in which you thought someone was not recovering from an emotional wound or injury fast enough, and you later learned something that increased your compassion for them?

Reflection Questions for “Why I see it this way” Anecdotes

1. What are experiences you have had or things you have observed that make it easy to see the link between past racial oppression and current circumstances?
2. Have you ever been emotionally affected by something longer than some people thought you should be affected? What was going on with you that they did not understand?

PHASE 2: ASK

1. What have you observed that reinforces the importance of people no longer talking about past racial difficulties?
2. What do you think is the harm that is caused to POC by talking about past racial difficulties? What is the harm that is caused to whites?
3. How do you think about the pros and cons of making connections between the past and present?
4. Are there historical events in your family or group’s past that you think get too much attention?
5. Have you ever seen a situation where an individual or a small group was affected by a past injury longer than you thought they should have been?

PHASE 3: CONNECT

1. Have you ever seen a situation where an individual or a small group was affected by a past injury longer than you thought they should have been?
   - » You have seen situations where you wondered whether some person or group was holding on to an injury longer than was healthy for them to do.
   - » You know of at least one situation where people successfully overcame regrettable actions or even victimization in their family's history.
   - » You can remember – without judging it - having a narrative about your life that felt robust and complete but that did not include some historical realities you later came to understand. (You will not reveal these realities until you transition to the Expand phase.)

Connect Anecdote One

Describe the situation:

____

____

Describe the key moment that illustrates the takeaway that connects to the skeptic's view:

____

____

Clarify the takeaway:

____

____

Connect Anecdote Two

Describe the situation:

____

____

Describe the key moment that illustrates the takeaway that connects to the skeptic's view:

____

____

Clarify the takeaway:

____

____

Connect Anecdote Three

Describe the situation:

____

____

Describe the key moment that illustrates the takeaway that connects to the skeptic's view:

____

____

Clarify the takeaway:

____

____

PHASE 4: EXPAND

Your goal is to convey an anecdote that compellingly makes the case for POC who connect past oppression to their current challenges.

One strategy is to relate a time when you observed someone incorrectly thinking that someone else was indulging a prior injury and choosing not to move on. Your key message most likely will focus on the way that non-injured parties often don't understand the depth of wounds to injured parties, and as a result accuse people of not moving forward. Once you have had a good conversation about this generally, you can explore whether there might be similar dynamics relevant to wounds between groups based on racial history.

Another strategy is to highlight the hidden benefits of history that have affected you. If people in your family used a societal benefit that excluded blacks (e.g. FHA, GI bill, and so on) you can describe how it helped you. After that, you can talk about discovering these programs' past racially discriminatory history, and how you felt about this. It is important not to overdo your reaction so it will not be dismissed as excessively guilt-oriented. Rather, position your discovery as pushing you to see the link between your families' benefit and other's difficulties, and thus increasing your understanding of why POC talk about the ongoing relevance of history.

If you told a prior narrative of your life before your awareness of history happened, now is the time to describe what you learned and how you realized that the impact of history can be hidden.

Expand Anecdote One

Describe the situation:

____

____

Describe the key moment that illustrates the takeaway that might expand the skeptic's view:

Clarify the takeaway:

Expand Anecdote Two

Describe the situation:

Describe the key moment that illustrates the takeaway that might expand the skeptic's view:

Clarify the takeaway:

Expand Anecdote Three

Describe the situation:

Describe the key moment that illustrates the takeaway that might expand the skeptic's view:

____

____

Clarify the takeaway:

____

____

OPTIONAL STEP: EXPLORE THE SEEMING CONTRADICTIONS

Perhaps it is true that	*AND*	it is also true that
A situation can have happened long ago	**and**	People can be affected by history in ways that are legitimate, but hard for others to see
One party can recover from an injury quicker than another party might from the same wound	**and**	It is possible for a party to think they have "put something behind them" when they actually haven't and they may still be affected later
An injured party can nurture a wound longer than is healthy	**and**	A party that has harmed someone are often underestimates the degree of damage they have caused

FINAL NOTES

Often, lurking beneath the desire that some skeptics have to stop talk about race is shame about being the embodiment of white racial history. This shame, which also affects allies, often undermines honest effective conversation. There will be a short discussion on shame in the Odds and Ends section.

RACISM-DENYING STATEMENT MODULE 5: IF PEOPLE OF COLOR WILL JUST ACT PROPERLY, LAW ENFORCEMENT WILL TREAT THEM FAIRLY.

ALTERNATE VERSIONS

- "Even if a few cops are bad, the overwhelming proportion treats everyone fairly."
- "The real problem is crime in the black community, not anything about the police."
- "If the police treated them that way, it must have been because they did something wrong."
- "People make too much out of the very rare cases of police abuse."

It may be helpful to convey that you agree with two points that skeptics often think demonstrate that racism does not exist:

- Most people in law enforcement attempt to do their jobs fairly.
- There is a crime problem in the black community that may have something to do with community norms, among other factors.

Conceding on these points – and perhaps even offering an experience that demonstrates these ideas – is likely to be helpful. These points do not undermine the experience you will later convey that helped you conclude that racial bias too frequently affects how law enforcement treats people.

PHASE 1: REFLECT

Reflection Questions for "I exactly half agree with you" Anecdotes

1. What is an early or powerful experience that reinforced a positive view of law enforcement? How did this experience compare to what you were taught about police as a child?
2. What is an experience where you observed law enforcement treating POC fairly, especially in a difficult situation?

3. Have you seen a situation where an officer was made noticeably less nervous (or more nervous) by the actions of a citizen?
4. What were you taught about crime and POC as a young person?

Reflection Questions for "I used to feel that way" Anecdotes

1. Do you remember thinking at some point that racism in law enforcement was extremely rare? Can you recall specific a time when you expressed this position, or when you strongly felt this was the case?
2. Do you remember a time when you thought that "the real problem" was black crime, and that any misconduct by law enforcement was a minor concern? What is an experience that can highlight that you once thought this way?
3. Have you ever been bothered by the Black Lives Matter movement? Have you ever felt that such protests (or the organization as a whole) are bad for POC or race relations?
4. Have you ever felt that a leader of color was "soft on crime" and not doing enough to improve police relations?

Reflection Questions for "But later, I realized" Anecdotes

1. Are there any beliefs you have about POC, and beliefs that you used to have but no longer have? Why and how did you change your perspective?
2. Have you ever had beliefs about the police (or the way they relate to communities of color) that you used to have, but no longer have? What experiences could help convey how and why your perspective changed?

Reflection Questions For "Why I see it this way" Anecdotes

1. If you have had one, describe an experience where you observed an encounter that increased your understanding of why so many POC do not trust law enforcement? How did this correspond to or oppose what you had previously learned about police?

2. Do you have any second-hand experiences from others you trust that tend to confirm a view of police as subject to racial bias?
3. Have you talked to a person of color who conveyed that they looked at law enforcement very differently than you do? What did they say that helped you understand their point of view?
4. What do you think are the main causes of distrust between people of color and law enforcement? What experiences cause you to answer like you do?
5. Have you ever observed white people having perceptions related to police and/or people of color that even many whites would find to be a distorted way of seeing things?

PHASE 2: ASK

1. What were you taught about law enforcement growing up? Can you remember any experiences that reinforced your views about the police?
2. How have your direct encounters with police gone, in general?
3. Have you ever witnessed an encounter with a person of color where that tended to confirm or counter your previous view of police?
4. When you hear people of color (or white folks on their behalf) blaming law enforcement for trust deficits, how do you feel? What is your perspective on the supposed problem of police misconduct? What is an experience, long ago or more recently, that reinforces your point of view?

PHASE 3: CONNECT

The following are some points of connectedness around which you might base a short story that validates something embedded within their racism-skeptical viewpoint.

- Not all police officers are bad; there are good cops out there.
- During an encounter with police, small personal decisions have a large impact on police officers, especially when they are nervous.
- There is problem of too much crime in many communities of color.

- It is important to prevent people who commit crimes from harming the community, no matter who they are.

If you have additional points of connection that might be helpful, please write them down. (We also encourage you to submit them to the project website so we can modify our materials.)

If you have any additional stories (second-hand ones are fine), jot down the key points.

An Opportunity To Go Into More Difficult Territory
It is important to note that there are some topics of race where the skeptic's surface sentiment actually emerges from a view about POC that is taboo to express directly. Race, crime, and law enforcement is clearly one of these topics.

Here are three examples of "taboo" beliefs that often lurk beneath the conversation.

1. People of color are inherently more prone to criminality.
2. The culture of people of color (especially blacks) prevents them from "normal" reactions to criminality and police.
3. Progressive people of color and whites sometimes exaggerate claims of police abuse.

If you decide to go to a deeper place, you will still need to find a connection point with the skeptic, and not judge them negatively for revealing their true beliefs to you. The most important thing is to convey an experience that illustrates you being affected by these beliefs, even if only subtly.

Some reflection questions that may help you form an anecdote if you are considering going deeper:

1. Was there a time or circumstance where you may have absorbed the message that POC were inherently problematic in the ways mentioned above? What drew you to thinking like that? (Note: it is important to describe this period when you had those thoughts without negatively judging yourself.)

2. What helped you develop a broader understanding of crime, punishment, and people of color? Were there any direct experiences that might have augmented what you learned by reading, listening to others, and so on? (Skeptics will be most receptive if you lead with as direct an experience as possible.)

Connect Anecdote One

Describe the situation:

Describe the key moment that illustrates the takeaway that connects to the skeptic's view:

Clarify the takeaway:

Connect Anecdote Two

Describe the situation:

Describe the key moment that illustrates the takeaway that connects to the skeptic's view:

Clarify the takeaway:

____

____

Connect Anecdote Three

Describe the situation:

____

____

Describe the key moment that illustrates the takeaway that connects to the skeptic's view:

____

____

Clarify the takeaway:

____

____

Experience Questions To Ask A Skeptic If You Plan To Go Deeper

1. Have you ever witnessed a person of color having a more negative attitude toward law enforcement than you thought was appropriate?
2. Can you discuss an experience where you perceived a high risk of crime in a community of color?
3. What were you taught about crime and POC as a young person?
4. Have you ever found yourself thinking that POC were inherently criminally-minded?

As noted in the economics module, you have the choice of going to deeper and more problematic places in your dialogue with the skeptic. It probably only makes sense if you have good reason to believe you can engage the person in an extended manner. And you may need to convey having had such troubling thoughts in the past so they know it is safe to admit to these thoughts.

PHASE 4: EXPAND

In pursuing your objective of broadening the skeptics' views of crime, punishment, and people of color, you might highlight:

- Unconscious bias against people of color by law enforcement officers
- Excessively harsh behavior by police toward people of color
- White people being treated leniently by police
- Conscious racism by law enforcement officers
- Situations where communities of color are disproportionately policed (this might include over- or under-policing)

Expand Anecdote One

Describe the situation:

____

____

Describe the key moment that illustrates the takeaway that might expand the skeptic's view:

____

____

Clarify the takeaway:

____

____

Expand Anecdote Two

Describe the situation:

____

____

Describe the key moment that illustrates the takeaway that might expand the skeptic's view:

____

____

Clarify the takeaway:

____

____

Expand Anecdote Three

Describe the situation:

____

____

Describe the key moment that illustrates the takeaway that might expand the skeptic's view:

____

____

Clarify the takeaway:

____

____

OPTIONAL STEP: EXPLORE THE SEEMING CONTRADICTIONS

Perhaps it is true that	*AND*	it is also true that
Crime in communities of color needs addressing	**and**	Police abuse in communities is worse than other places and needs addressing
Many police treat everyone fairly	**and**	Some police are more likely to be abusive when interacting with POC
Almost all cops try hard to treat everyone the same way	**and**	Unconscious bias against POC can affect cops even though they don't intend this
Activists can use claims of police abuse cynically	**and**	Police abuse in communities of color is still a real problem

FINAL NOTES

At the right time, bring up facts, data, illustrations, and other non-experiential types of knowledge to expand the conversation.

One way of organizing your self-education about race and police is to think about three broad classes of knowledge about race and law enforcement:

- Racial bias affecting perceptions by and about law enforcement
- Statistical data about discrepant treatment and outcomes of people of color
- Historical data about relations between police and people of color

RACISM-DENYING STATEMENT MODULE 6: VERY FEW PEOPLE ARE CONSCIOUSLY RACIST ANY MORE.

ALTERNATE VERSIONS

- "We have been in a post-racial era since Obama got elected."
- "Every white person I know tries to be colorblind."

The decline of overt white bigotry as expressed in surveys and in conversation has declined dramatically in the past five decades, so creating a sense of connection by conceding this should be easy and useful. It might be valuable to brush up on a few facts from survey data to buttress any personal experiences you have that demonstrate this change in attitudes.

At the same time, there is ample survey data showing that a significant proportion of white adults still hold bigoted views, as has been noted. When it comes to the Expand phase, start as usual with one to two clear experiences you have showing that these attitudes are still around. Do this before relating whatever factoids you know about troubling attitudes which are still circulating.

PHASE 1: REFLECT

Reflection Questions for "I exactly half agree with you" Anecdotes

1. Recall a story about witnessing explicit racism that you think would be much less likely to happen today because of different social norms.
2. If during your childhood you were ever exposed to an adult who tried to teach you to be racist in a way that would not likely happen today, jot some notes about your memories.
3. If you have a story from at least twenty years ago from a person of color who experienced explicit racism in a way that you imagine would be much less likely to happen today, write down the key elements of that story.
4. If you have ever known a person of color who, in your opinion, was over- estimating the degree of animus toward people of color, jot a few notes about what happened to make you come to that conclusion.

5. If you have any other experience that leads you to think such feelings have declined over the past two to four decades, jot some notes about this experience.

Reflection Questions for "I used to feel that way" Anecdotes

1. If you used to believe that very few people were still racist, recall a time when you expressed this opinion in a conversation or were focused mentally on this idea.
2. Have you ever been with a group of people – whether briefly or on an extended basis – where racist views were considered normal and natural?

Reflection Questions for "But later, I realized" Anecdotes

1. If you have any experiences of witnessing expressions of racial bigotry that were eye opening for you, jot a few notes about them here.
2. When you went from believing racially troubling views to a new understanding, what kind of feelings did you have about how you used to think about this?

Reflection Questions for "Why I see it this way" Anecdotes

1. Jot down notes about 2-3 experiences in the last ten years that illustrate a white person having unambiguous prejudice against a person of color. If you have more than one to choose from, focus on perfecting stories that have strong impact because the prejudice is egregious, the people are powerful, or the story is more recent.
2. If you have a second-hand story from a person of color (or a white person) about encountering explicit bigotry, describe it.
3. Jot down notes about 1-2 of your own experiences in the last ten years (better if more recent) that confirm for you that explicit bigotry is not completely a thing of the past.
4. If another person has told you about an experience related to continued bigotry within the last ten years (the more recent the better), make note of it.

PHASE 2: ASK

1. What have you experienced that lets you know that there is much less bigotry than there was just after the civil rights movement? What changes have you seen in your lifetime?
2. Have you ever seen people of color over-estimating the amount of animus aimed toward them? How did you come to that conclusion?
3. Do you think that the proportion of people who have negative views of other racial groups actually matters, or that this does not make a difference?
4. Do you think that different groups tend to underestimate, overestimate, or accurately estimate how common such perspectives are? Do you think that different identity groups might make mistakes about this?
5. Have you ever seen evidence that someone harbored negative feelings toward people of color? (If you ask this challenging question, only do so AFTER asking questions that encourage storytelling that is aligned with their point of view.)

PHASE 3: CONNECT

Your primary task is to convey to the skeptic that you know that explicit bigotry against POC has dramatically declined in the last few decades. A factoid that might help you in the Connect phase is that according to a 1990 University of Illinois Chicago survey, 66% of whites thought that blacks were less intelligent than whites. The same survey found these percentages had declined by more than half by 2014, to 32%.

Some options might be:

- Share about a personal experience that happened long ago where a white person demonstrated their bigoted views that you think would be very unlikely to happen now.
- Describe a time you thought that a person of color was overestimating - even for understandable reasons - even for understandable reasons – the amount of racism in society or in a situation.

- Share your perspective on some event or situation that indicates that social bigotry has declined significantly.

Connect Anecdote One

Describe the situation:

____

____

Describe the key moment that illustrates the takeaway that connects to the skeptic's view:

____

____

Clarify the takeaway:

____

____

Connect Anecdote Two

Describe the situation:

____

____

Describe the key moment that illustrates the takeaway that connects to the skeptic's view:

____

____

Clarify the takeaway:

____

____

Connect Anecdote Three

Describe the situation:

____

____

Describe the key moment that illustrates the takeaway that connects to the skeptic's view:

____

____

Clarify the takeaway:

____

____

PHASE 4: EXPAND

Offer 1-2 experiences that illustrate how you came to realize that old-fashioned bigotry against POC is still a real factor in American life.

As you search through your memory for experiences to choose from, remember that a skeptic may require a high threshold of proof that racial animus was at play and that it resulted in mistreatment. Ideally, your story will be such that any reasonable person would conclude that racial animus was at play in the situation. Having heard a salesperson in a store talking about not liking to serve "those people" is strongly suggestive of animus; hearing such statements and witnessing the salesperson mistreat someone is more persuasive. (If you can only report the "those people" comment and not actual treatment, a skeptic may accuse you of operating as the "speech police.")

Of course, you may not have each of these types of events in your experience. You may not have seen such mistreatment or you may not have heard white people make statements in all-white settings that confirm their bigoted beliefs. Your goal is to construct a series of brief anecdotes that are difficult to dismiss.

While it is not ideal, second-hand stories are better than only a hunch that racial bigotry and animus persist. Hopefully, you have trust-based and close relationships with some POC. If you do, there may be a time when it is appropriate to ask them if they have been on the receiving end of this kind of bigotry. If you decide to ask about such experiences, be sensitive about the possibility that you are asking them to recount something that may have been very painful. You want to make sure they do not feel that you are asking them for "racism porn." It will be useful to explain that you want to hear about this not only because you want to understand their experience of race, but also for the specific purpose of having a stronger tool to move skeptics along.

There is also a value in second-hand stories from other white allies—the more recent, the better.

Expand Anecdote One

Describe the situation:

____

____

Describe the key moment that illustrates the takeaway that might expand the skeptic's view:

____

____

Clarify the takeaway:

____

____

Expand Anecdote Two

Describe the situation:

____

____

Describe the key moment that illustrates the takeaway that might expand the skeptic's view:

____

____

Clarify the takeaway:

____

____

Expand Anecdote Three

Describe the situation:

____

____

Describe the key moment that illustrates the takeaway that might expand the skeptic's view:

____

____

Clarify the takeaway:

____

____

OPTIONAL STEP: EXPLORE THE SEEMING CONTRADICTIONS

Perhaps it is true that	*AND*	it is also true that
Overt racism has declined a lot in the past few decades	**and**	There is still a surprising amount of racism by whites against people of color
Sometimes POC have not fully accepted the reality that overt bigotry has declined	**and**	POC still experience the impact of bigotry and don't always talk about it to whites
There are developments that have happened that are evidence of racial progress we can all be proud of	**and**	There is a evidence that our progress on race is only incomplete, and society is still affected by the severe racial inequities of the past
Many white people can be innocent of racism	**and**	There is still benefit from being white
Some of the discourse around white privilege can be distorted	**and**	The concept still might have some validity

FINAL NOTES

You should make conscious choices about when it is most effective to shift the conversation to data, since this rarely changes minds. In this case, however, there is very strong data that supports both the racism- skeptical and the racism-acknowledging perspectives. There is a wealth of survey data that demonstrates levels of animus expressed by whites has declined sharply in recent decades. Other data shows that a remarkably large number of white people believe that some or most POC are inferior on an important dimension such as intelligence, industriousness, or criminal-mindedness. As has been mentioned, evidence shows a substantial proportion of whites hold some level of distaste for certain groups of color and disfavor intermarriage, living in neighborhoods with substantial numbers of POC, or sending their children to school with them.

As you present this data, be mindful of how much you need to make your point. Some people will change their mind due to an overwhelming mountain of evidence that contradicts their point of view. However, other people will be made uncomfortable by hearing too much that disconfirms their beliefs, and the Backfire Effect will rule the day. It is important to stop presenting evidence at the right time.

Here Are Some Facts That May Be Helpful. Use With Caution.
Sometimes reframing can be helpful as you are marshaling data. For instance, some anti-racism advocates discuss the more than 20 percent of whites who view blacks as inferior. They refer to numbers of blacks in America (37 million as of 2017) and compare it to the number of whites who think blacks are inferior – 38 million, which is 20 percent of 196 million.

Here is another example of a potentially savvy reframe: There is reliable data that shows a substantial proportion of white Hillary Clinton supporters thought blacks are intellectually inferior and an even greater proportion of white Donald Trump supporters that thought the same way. When talking to a politically conservative skeptic, one tactic that some allies take is to cite the Clinton statistic to illustrate that a non-trivial number of whites hold these views. This strategy plays to the common narrative that the "real racists" are liberals. You can feign ignorance for the moment about the proportion of Trump supporters who think similarly (a significantly higher proportion), and encourage them to look this up for your next conversation.[16]

If the skeptic becomes resistant to more data, it may be time to remind

16 https://www.reuters.com/article/us-usa-election-race/exclusive-trump-supporters-more-likely-to-view-blacks-negatively-reuters-ipsos-poll-idUSKCN0ZE2SW?feedType=RSS&feedNam

them that you conceded that explicit bigotry has significantly declined over time. As needed, remind them that you are not trying to judge that their perspective is incorrect, rather, you are trying to add to their sense of truth with more information.

Get them to explore whether there is a good way of integrating all that this exchange has covered. The most obvious is to reiterate that bigotry has declined, yet exists to a significant extent and still affects POC. Be attentive to when to stop the conversation for resumption later. For instance, a natural corollary to the reality that many whites are still bigoted is that POC naturally wonder if the person in front of them is one of the 20% who thinks that they are inferior. White privilege lurks around this reality, since worrying about this animus is a burden that you and the skeptic don't have to contend with. But, it may or may not be helpful to bring this issue up.

---

e=topNews&utm_source=twitter&utm_medium=Social)

RACISM-DENYING STATEMENT MODULE 7: IT IS VITAL THAT AMERICA DRASTICALLY REDUCE IMMIGRATION SO THAT WE CAN RETURN TO OUR CULTURAL GREATNESS.

ALTERNATE VERSIONS

- "In previous generations, immigrants would focus on assimilation into an existing culture. We only need immigrants who are willing to do that."
- "Immigration is taking opportunities away from Americans who need them."
- "Diversity might be nice but it has gone too far. We need to return to an America with a common culture."

While there is a broad set of reasons (some valid, some spurious, and some based on animus) for supporting cutbacks in immigration, common themes you are likely to hear include:

- America culture is fragmenting and too much immigration makes this worse.
- Too many immigrants refuse to learn English or to otherwise assimilate.
- Immigrants, especially undocumented ones, take opportunities away from Americans.
- Undocumented immigrants erode respect for the rule of law.

Some points that you should consider conveying to connect to the skeptic after learning more about their perspective:

- It is understandable that good-hearted white people sometimes see immigrants as other.
- Having immigrants in the country makes our lives more complicated and sometimes it is unsettling.
- It can certainly feel like many opportunities are going to immigrants.
- It is possible for an individual to favor decreased immigration and have that sentiment not be mostly about bias/racism.

You can concede these points, without undermining what you want to convey through experience, which is probably one of these three points:

- White people have to be careful to keep aversion to those different than us in check.
- Immigration involves many benefits to society.
- Your perspective on immigration has evolved over the course of your life.

PHASE 1: REFLECT

Reflection Questions for "I exactly half agree with you" Anecdotes

1. Have you ever felt like the presence of non-Americans was weakening important aspects of American culture?
2. Have you ever felt that we might be doing not enough for some Americans citizens and too much for people born elsewhere?
3. Do you ever find it irritating that we often have to accommodate non-English speakers or people with very thick accents?
4. Are there any other experiences you have had that might help you connect with someone who feels like America is changing too fast or is too welcoming of people from other countries?

Reflection Questions for "I used to feel that way" Anecdotes

1. Can you remember a time when you were much more averse to immigrants personally than you are now? What is an example of time when your experience was affected by this aversion?
2. Was there a time when you were more conservative on immigration policy than you are now? What is an example of a moment where you were in touch with that perspective?

Reflection Questions for "But later, I realized" Anecdotes

1. If you previously had a different view of immigration than you do now, what experiences did you have that helped change your mind?

2. How do you look back on your previous viewpoint on immigration? What were some factors that had been affecting you that you did not before realize?

Reflection Questions for Helping You Prepare a Story That Supports Your Perspective on Immigration

1. Jot down notes from family stories that illustrate the value of immigration to the country.
2. Jot down notes from family stories that illustrate the way that immigrants of a previous era were looked down upon.
3. What is an example of time when an immigrant (preferably undocumented) noticeably enriched the life of you or someone you know?
4. How is your perspective on immigration connected to your sense of religious obligation, if you feel that? Are there any experiences that underscore that connection?
5. Have you ever seen a situation where a less competent/capable white person was able to keep a job that a more capable immigrant could do better?

PHASE 2: ASK

Whether you ask about how they initially formed their views or more recent experiences that tend to support their position, the most important thing is that you ask the question(s) in a way that does not make the skeptic feel negatively judged.

Some potentially useful questions are:

1. When did you first start feeling like we had too much immigration? Was there any particular experience that first drove this point home?
2. How was immigration talked about in your home growing up? Was the idea that we have to avoid too much immigration a shared idea in your family? Have you ever had a perspective about immigration that was different than the one you have now? What experience did you have that changed your mind?

3. What was an experience in the past 5 years that has driven home the importance of cutting back on immigration?

4. Are there any experiences that are not dramatic but only somewhat irritating – even a small experience like hearing "Press 1 for English" – that amplify your view about immigration?

PHASE 3: CONNECT

Determine your Connect stories for a conversation about immigration by reviewing the prompt questions and deciding which you could tell most compellingly.

Connect Anecdote One

Describe the situation:

____

____

Describe the key moment that illustrates the takeaway that connects to the skeptic's view:

____

____

Clarify the takeaway:

____

____

Connect Anecdote Two

Describe the situation:

____

____

Describe the key moment that illustrates the takeaway that connects to the skeptic's view:

____

____

Clarify the takeaway:

____

____

Connect Anecdote Three

Describe the situation:

____

____

Describe the key moment that illustrates the takeaway that connects to the skeptic's view:

____

____

Clarify the takeaway:

____

____

PHASE 4: EXPAND

Your objective is to share 1-2 anecdotes that illuminate why you oppose the anti-immigration sentiment that is increasingly common in some parts of the white community. While it is fine to base this feeling on opposing the anti-immigrant sentiment, it will likely be more effective if you have experiences that reinforce a pro-immigration position. Make conscious decisions about whether your story focuses on legal vs. illegal immigration.

If you are going to focus on illegal immigration, it may be useful before that to signal that you have respect for the rule of law and/or authority. Many skeptics' views on undocumented immigration are a mix of xenophobia and faithfulness to authority structures. If your goal is to influence them to be compassionate to migrants who are undocumented, you will likely be better off if you have reminded them that you place some value on legal authority.

Expand Anecdote One

Describe the situation:

____

____

Describe the key moment that illustrates the takeaway that might expand the skeptic's view:

____

____

Clarify the takeaway:

____

____

Expand Anecdote Two

Describe the situation:

____

____

Describe the key moment that illustrates the takeaway that might expand the skeptic's view:

____

____

Clarify the takeaway:

____

____

Expand Anecdote Three

Describe the situation:

____

____

Describe the key moment that illustrates the takeaway that might expand the skeptic's view:

____

____

Clarify the takeaway:

____

____

OPTIONAL STEP: EXPLORE THE SEEMING CONTRADICTIONS

Perhaps it is true that	*AND*	it is also true that
Modern life makes the challenges of assimilating easier for native born citizens	**and**	The vast majority of immigrants are assimilating just as fast as previous generations of immigrants
There are some jobs for which immigrants do out-compete native born citizens	**and**	There are some jobs that are necessary but that native born Americans refuse wages that immigrants will accept
Having millions of undocumented immigrants decreases many people's sense that laws should be obeyed	**and**	Rounding up undocumented immigrants with long ties to the community undermines many people's sense that their community is fair and cohesive

RACISM-DENYING STATEMENT MODULE 8: THOSE ATHLETES WHO PROTEST DURING THE NATIONAL ANTHEM ARE DISRESPECTING THE NATION, THE FLAG, AND THE TROOPS.

ALTERNATE VERSIONS

- "Any athlete who does not stand during the anthem is demonstrating that s/he is ungrateful for the opportunities this country gave them."
- "Any person who cares about this country stands and does not use the anthem as a time to make a statement."

Creating an effective dialogue through storytelling on this topic has an additional conversational element that will be described.

To connect with the skeptic, it is usually helpful to show alignment on issues of loyalty and order that they are likely to resonate with. This may involve telling an anecdote demonstrating that:

- You think patriotism is important.
- Sometimes you are emotionally moved by your love of America.
- You have had moments when you were bothered by the way that someone was protesting a situation.

In the Expand part of the process, it is useful to get the skeptic's awareness around the fact that "outgroups" have less prestige than "ingroups." The best way to do this is to relate an anecdote about you or someone you know being in an outgroup, and most importantly, having a more complicated sense of loyalty in the setting than member of the ingroups.

After telling stories that will help the skeptic agree that outgroups often have different senses of loyalty than ingroups, your next task is to relate experiences that made you empathize with the fact that many POC see themselves as an outgroup. The point of those shifts in focus is to get the skeptic to understand why you have some empathy for people protesting, even though you love America.

PHASE 1: REFLECT

Reflection Questions for "I exactly half agree with you" Anecdotes

1. If possible, describe an experience where you were emotionally moved during the national anthem or a similarly patriotic song.
2. If possible, describe an experience, by yourself or in a group, where you felt a great deal of pride in the United States.
3. If possible, describe an experience of feeling very happy to be an American.
4. What aspect of American values gives you the greatest feeling of satisfaction? Why? Describe a moment when you felt this satisfaction very deeply.
5. If you have had one, describe a time when someone was conducting a protest and you felt it was inappropriate or it made you uncomfortable.

Reflection Questions for "I used to feel that way" Anecdotes

1. If it happened, describe a conversation or a moment when you looked at national symbols and/or protests about them similar to the way that your skeptic does.
2. In the past, have you ever noticed yourself being angry at someone for not being as patriotic as you were at the time?

Reflection Questions for "But later, I realized" Anecdotes

1. If there was a key moment when you shifted how you looked at national symbols or protests, jot some notes about it.
2. If you ever adjusted your thinking to become less judgmental of people who think about patriotism differently that you do or did, jot a few notes about how your thinking changed.

If your moment involved a shift in how you feel about the U.S.– as opposed to its symbols – it may not be in your interest to focus on this anecdote. It is highly unlikely that you will get the skeptic to have empathy for you if you tell a story about how you realized, for example, the troubling moral implications of the U.S. history of violent colonialism. However, if the change in your perspective was about national symbols or even better, about other people's protests, you are more likely to avoid the defensiveness of your skeptic.

Reflection Questions for "Why I see it this way" Anecdotes

1. If you have one, describe an experience where you had a family member who generated more complicated feelings within you than did other family members? When and how did you notice that you felt differently than others in the family?
2. Describe a time when you felt a part of community but also had some misgivings about it, because you had problems that other members did not.
3. Describe any complicated feelings about your high school or college experience. Were you in an outgroup? If so, how did that affect your feelings about the school? If you were not in an outgroup but were friends with someone who was, what did you learn about loyalty from this experience?
4. If you were in an ingroup and did not understand the complaints of some people in an outgroup, describe your perspectives and experience of that situation. (Examples might be high school, college, work, or a community large enough to have sub-groups with different levels of status).
5. Have you ever been in an outgroup in a community? If so, did this experience contribute to you and others having different feelings of loyalty and affection toward the community than those not in outgroups?
6. Have you ever had an extensive conversation with a POC with complicated feelings about America? If so, try to remember any of their experiences that helped you understand why. If you can remember a particular moment when you poignantly understood why many POC feel ambivalent in their patriotism, describe that moment as best as you can.
7. If you have done so, describe a time when you participated in a

protest that was designed to make some people feel disrupted or uncomfortable. Describe why you thought that the protest was worth it, despite the fact that uncomfortable feelings were experienced by others. Did it bother you that this discomfort was a result of the protest?

Conversational Flow
The basic strategy for this conversation flows from the following logic:

A racism skeptic is not likely to have done a thought experiment about how it might feel to experience America through the eyes of an outgroup. You may encourage them to mentally try it. One strategy is to encourage them to think about a time when you were in an outgroup in a social situation. For instance, many people have had this experience in school or community activities. Others may recall a family situation where they were not in an outgroup, but they had a more complicated experience of the family.

Your goal is to help them see in a non-race-based situation that people who have multi-layered experiences have a sense of loyalty that is more complicated than those whose was straightforwardly positive. After illustrating this idea with your own experience, you may want to ask them if they can relate to it from some experience they have had of being in an outgroup.

If you can get the skeptic to acknowledge that people's sense of loyalty can be complicated – especially if they are in an outgroup - then your task is to get them to acknowledge that POC have a different experience of the nation, and this adds a complicating factor to their loyalty.

PHASE 2: ASK

Your goal is to ask the skeptic about experiences that undergird and illustrate their opinion about patriotism and protest. One option is to ask them to tell you two short stories, one about a moment when they were feeling particularly patriotic, and one that shows them being bothered by people protesting something that is supposed to serve as a collective symbol.

The first story is worth asking about because it may be easier for you to show alignment than the second story. If you have ever had a moment of national pride, patriotism, or even gratitude to be an American, it will likely be useful to briefly relive this moment so that your skeptic knows you are capable of feeling these things.

Questions about the Skeptic's Experience of Patriotism and Protests

1. Tell me about a time when you were particularly filled with your love of country.
2. Tell me about a time when you heard the national anthem and it really moved you emotionally.
3. What happens when you see or hear about athletes kneeling to protest police abuse during the anthem? How do you feel? Do your feelings change depending on whether they are professional or not?
4. Has your perspective about the athletes' protests changed since they first started? If so, how and why?
5. Have you ever been part of a group that included folks who appeared to feel that they were not part of the "ingroup"? Did it ever seem like the people in the outgroup had a different sense of loyalty than folks in the ingroup?
6. Have you ever been a part of a group (in your family, in a school, etc.) where you felt you were not in the "ingroup"? If so, did you ever think that your loyalty toward the community felt different than the loyalty of the ingroup members?

PHASE 3: CONNECT

At this point, you want to make sure they know that you sometimes feel patriotic. This is probably not the best time to discuss whatever misgivings you have around the history of U.S. government misdeeds, foreign or domestic. Instead, relate instances when you felt happy or even proud to be a member of your national community.

When you get to an experience of ambivalent loyalty, it is probably best if it is NOT about America as a whole, but about some other community or institution that you have been connected to.

Connect Anecdote One

Describe the situation:

____

____

Describe the key moment that illustrates the takeaway that connects to the skeptic's view:

____

____

Clarify the takeaway:

____

____

Connect Anecdote Two

Describe the situation:

____

____

Describe the key moment that illustrates the takeaway that connects to the skeptic's view:

____

____

Clarify the takeaway:

____

____

Connect Anecdote Three

Describe the situation:

____

____

Describe the key moment that illustrates the takeaway that connects to the skeptic's view:

____

____

Clarify the takeaway:

____

____

PHASE 4: EXPAND

The Expand phase for this module is more complex than for the other modules in this workbook.

Expand Move 1: The first task is to get the skeptic to acknowledge that, setting aside race/racism, people in outgroups in a human community tend to have a more complicated sense of loyalty to that community than people who are in in-groups.

Examples include:

- Groups considered less valuable in a school settings (e.g. Nerds, Geeks)

- Members of low prestige sororities or fraternities
- Step-family members in a family that prizes blood relations
- Junior employees in an agency that values seniority

The most effective anecdote is one where you can compellingly make the case that people in an outgroup (including perhaps yourself) appeared to feel a lessened and/or more complicated sense of loyalty that those in the ingroup. If possible, you should try to make a subtle connection between the experience of being in the outgroup and having a different sense of connectedness to the system in question.

If possible, ask the skeptic questions to explore whether they are familiar with the way that members of outgroups feel differently than others. Maybe they have been in an outgroup, or have had friends or family members who have.

Once you have gotten them to acknowledge that members of outgroups have more complicated feelings of loyalty than ingroup members, you can progress to the next phase of the conversation.

Expand Move 2: Relate anecdotes that suggest that many people of color understandably feel they are in an outgroup

Your objective is to manage the conversation in a way that moves the skeptic to seeing why POC might see themselves as an out-group in the U.S.

One strategy that many allies have said is useful is to engage the skeptic in a version of the "Imagine if you were a person of color." Citing both historical factors (slavery, lynchings, forced segregation, etc.) and current factors (large pluralities of whites find blacks and Hispanics inferior, discrepancies in law enforcement interventions, studies that demonstrate the pervasiveness of employment discrimination) may be helpful.

While these are helpful sometimes, you may have more success if you can relate personal anecdotes, such as:

- Instances when you witnessed a person of color being treated unfairly
- A time when a person of color discussed their general sense of being regarded as other
- A second-hand story of unfair treatment from a person of color

Your objective is to encourage the skeptic to acknowledge that POC often see themselves as part of an outgroup, and thus, have complicated feelings of loyalty just as members of other outgroups often do.

OPTIONAL PHASE: EXPLORE THE SEEMING CONTRADICTIONS

It may be helpful to direct the skeptic's attention toward the possibility that their perspective on the anthem protest is reasonable—and that other perspectives on the protests are also reasonable. The following table may help you pursue this line of conversation.

Perhaps it is true that	*AND*	it is also true that
It is reasonable for members of in-groups to have uncomplicated feelings of loyalty	**and**	It is reasonable for members of out-groups to have complicated feelings of loyalty
The flag and the anthem legitimately represent the fulfilled ideals of America for some people	**and**	The flag and the anthem legitimately represent unfulfilled ideals of America for some people
Some people experience standing during the anthem as honoring Americans who died serving their country	**and**	Some people experience kneeling during the anthem as honoring Americans who died unfairly at the hands of the government

FINAL NOTES

- The third stanza of the Star-Spangled Banner mentions slavery with no discernible ambivalence about the tensions between slavery and the "land of the free."
- The association between the anthem and the military is a relatively recent development, spurred in part by branding decisions made by the NFL in 2009.

ADDITIONAL WORKSHEET FOR PROBLEMATIC STATEMENTS NOT COVERED IN THIS WORKBOOK

RACIALLY PROBLEMATIC STATEMENT

(It is best to depict the statement, not just describe it. Put it in quotes)

REFLECTION QUESTIONS

Are there one or more things that are true and arguably embedded within the statement?

1.

2.

Have you ever thought this way, or close to this way?

If you have ever thought this way, what happened that moved you from thinking this way?

What is an observation of some reality about race/racism related to the statement that skeptics tend to deny, downplay, or are just not sufficiently aware of?

CONSTRUCTING CONNECT AND EXPAND STORIES

Jot a few notes that represent the core elements of a Connect story about this issue here.

Write a few notes that represent the core elements of an Expand story about this issue here.

FINAL THOUGHTS ON THE MODULES

Congratulations! Whether you read through all of the modules or just one, you are now much more prepared to have a productive encounter with a racism skeptic. This is particularly true if you have actually completed the reflection exercises and constructed the Connect and Expand stories, instead of just reading over the worksheets.

The most important next step for you is actually practicing your anecdotes, perhaps with a live human being. (It would not be a bad idea to practice your stories by yourself, just to get used to hearing the words coming out of your mouth.) It is not vital to your first attempt to marshal these stories be with a racism skeptic. Practicing the stories with another ally – whether or not you tell them in advance about what you are doing – will be a very useful way to prepare for the moment when someone makes a racially troubling statement that you do not expect.

Reading each of the next two major sections of this workbook will be valuable for your journey as an ally, because this is likely to broaden your options in how to manage conversations. There are some specific subsections that are particularly important if you are pressed for time and want to quickly refine how you show up. The Othering subsection of the Primer gives guidance for talking about the fundamental psychological dynamic behind racism and other isms that mentally turn people into "other than me." The Shame subsection in Odds and Ends may help you recognize an impediment to your past and future effectiveness in engaging skeptics. After you have developed Connect and Expand stories, it might be useful to review the Moral Frameworks subsection of Odds and Ends and make some tweaks to boost their effectiveness. Also, the Closing Encouragements may keep you motivated to stay on the ally path.

PART THREE: THE ALLY COACHING CURRICULUM

Part Three prepares allies who want to intentionally focus on a person's racial awareness and strengthen it over a period time.

THE PRIMER

KEY CONCEPTS OF INTERPERSONAL RACISM

This primer prepares you to go on an intentional conversational journey with a white racism skeptic or someone who is significantly less racism-aware than you are.

The usefulness of this primer is somewhat different than that of The Modules in Part Two. The previous section contains a number of separate modules with guidance about how to pivot from an unexpected racially-problematic remark – one that is either racially prejudiced or minimizes racism's existence - to an exchange or set of conversations that might influence how a racism skeptic thinks. It is important that white allies are prepared to create moments of dialogue in this improvisational way.

The perspective of this project is that the obligation of white allies does not stop with leveraging these unexpected opportunities to influence racism skeptics. In order for public opinion to be changed on large scale, the work of white allies should also involve pro-actively coaching people up a path of learning about racism and their role in dismantling it. Every ally should have a clear but flexible plan – that is, a curriculum - for the sequence of concepts that they will try to get their skeptics to understand. One day every year (e.g. January 1, April 4: the anniversary of Martin Luther King's assassination, July 4), allies against racism should identify one or more specific people that they will be working on influencing during the coming year. This primer is intended to serve as the foundation of a curriculum that will guide an intentional conversational journey that you might take with one or more people.

The concepts of this primer are ordered in a way that is likely to work for skeptics. The structure is based on decades of professional experience leading racial dialogue processes, so it is on a solid foundation. But in truth, this curriculum has not been tested by thousands of untrained allies working on skeptics. So, you should regard it as a guide for your coaching. However, like any good teacher or coach, you will need to make smart choices in the moment about how to move the specific people you are working on up a ladder of understanding. The hope is that you can stay connected to this project and give feedback on what strategies work best, in what order, and under what conditions.

The concepts and their order are as follows:

1. **Othering** – the phenomenon of consciously or semi-consciously seeing people in other groups as different than oneself;
2. **Unconscious Bias** – deeply ingrained views that people have of other groups. These views operate below our conscious level of awareness;
3. **Attribution Error** – the tendency of people to see other people's behavior as reflecting some personal or group characteristic. In contrast, when looking at our own behavior, we tend to see what we do as a response to the circumstances in the situation;
4. **Racial Anxiety** – people's worry that others will see them through a racial lens;
5. **Unearned Racial Advantage (commonly called "white privilege")** – the benefits of being treated as "normal" or superior because of one's racial status;
6. **Racial Threat** – worry that social and/or political developments will harm the status of my racial group;
7. **Racial Backlash/Denial** – actions taken by a group in response to the perception that another group has altered the racial order;
8. **Institutional Racism** – the way that an organization or sector of society operates in a way that consistently creates a disadvantage for some groups compared to other groups;
9. **Structural Racism** – the way that the occurrence of institutional racism in separate sectors can combine to compound racial disparities and make it more difficult for any one person, institution, or sector to combat disparities;

10. **Racial Equity** – a potential future condition in which opportunities, chances, and outcomes for people cannot be reliably predicted by their racial background.

It is important to distinguish concepts #1 through 7 from concepts #8 through 11, with respect to the kind of conversation allies can and need to have with racism skeptics. Concepts #1 through 7 (othering, unconscious bias, attribution error, racial anxiety, unearned racial advantage, racial threat, racial backlash/denial) are all social-psychological dynamics that can be directly experienced at the individual level, though seeing this may require reflection and discernment. As such, it is possible for an ally to review his or her experiences closely, perhaps talk to a few other allies, and be able to explain how they and others have directly experienced these ideas. The advantage of this conversation is that the ally can tell personal stories about feeling emotions and noticing their and others' behavior, and such storytelling can be very influential.

Racial backlash/denial lies between the individual and cumulative concepts. People making decisions rarely see themselves as affected by these factors at the time. They can sometimes see how these factors influenced them at a later time when they have more distance from the immediate circumstance. Often though, racial backlash and denial are very visible when looking at the way people make decisions, even though most of them would report that racial factors are not affecting their thinking.

In contrast, concepts #8 through 11 (institutional racism, structural racism, and racial equity) require an even higher level of abstraction. Institutional and structural racism are inherently more abstract concepts, in that they describe the result of cumulative behavior of large numbers of people acting on behalf of large organizations. Finally, racial equity is an imagined state that does not exist but that is the goal of much anti-racism work.

So while these latter four concepts are very much grounded in reality, recognizing them relies to a much greater extent rely on statistics, historical interpretation, or other sources of insight that are not as tightly bound to direct personal experiences. As a result, when trying to influence a skeptic to see these realities, you will likely need to rely on external data. As has been discussed, people can have a great deal of skepticism about sources of information that they think are biased against their existing view of the world, regardless of how much objective expertise these sources rely on. You are better off first having conversations about the concepts that you can examine together through

The anti-racism movement does not really know which kinds of skeptics are better served by starting with the personal topics and which are better served by staring with the community and institution issues. Allies will need to experiment with different approaches and observe their results to figure out the best strategies.

There is a contrasting view that suggests the above might be incorrect. Our workshop participants have said that within the context of workshops, some racism skeptics can more easily think about racism if the topic is not approached in a way that personally implicates them. It is possible that for some skeptics, raising societal issues before interpersonal ones is more effective, even in one-on-one conversations. Again, there have not been large-scale experiments about how to combat skepticism about racism. The anti-racism movement does not really know which kinds of skeptics are better served by starting with the personal topics and which are better served by starting with the community and institution issues. Allies will need to experiment with different approaches and observe their results to figure out the best strategies.

In light of that, this workbook includes brief discussions of these data-based concepts, but with the knowledge that allies may not be able to get each skeptic to go that far on the journey of understanding. If this material were a subject taught at a university, concepts #1-7 are the undergraduate prerequisites, while concepts #8-11 are advanced courses.

This distinction reinforces an important point about the nature of ally work. While this project encourages white allies to learn as much as possible about the nature of racism from those who studied it, allies can make a good deal of progress influencing racism skeptics by strategically having conversations that bring those experiences to bear. Too many white allies think they are insufficiently qualified to lead other whites along a path of greater understanding. If you believe that racism is an important national problem, you are ready to be a positive force with those you know to be skeptical about that. You merely need to do some focused reflection on your own experiences, think about a strategy for deploying them along with brief explanations of basic racial concepts, and then learn what happens in actual conversations.

THE CHALLENGE OF MOVING SOMEONE THROUGH THEIR SKEPTICISM ABOUT RACISM BEING REAL

The task of moving a racism skeptic through their tendency to deny the reality of racism is challenging because of the way that many white people have been conditioned. As noted in the introduction, the civil rights movement was very effective in showing white America that racism was a contradiction to the ideals of America as well as a collective moral sin. Unfortunately, despite the purposeful effort by the movement to convey that this sin existed both at the level of individuals' hearts and collective outcomes, the white community mostly internalized the notion of racism as a problem of individuals and of explicit institutional policies. For a brief period (perhaps from about 1965 until 1980), some portions of the white community looked at the community conditions and the lack of opportunity for POC as also a societal problem worthy of action. Unfortunately, many white people reverted back to – or perhaps never transcended – the perspective that the problems that POC confront are of their own making. Tens of millions of whites see racial disparities as unfortunate realities that are not connected to societal racism, to white America, and certainly not to themselves.

This tendency of many whites to blame POC for their
been around for centuries. It is perhaps less preval
fact, the general level of animus in the white pop
undergo a major improvement between the early
(This was discussed in Part Two.) During this period
idea of harboring explicitly prejudiced views – i.e. being
anathema to many whites. Even so, very significant numbers
resentment and condescension.

Arguably, the civil rights movement and white America's reaction to it overshot the mark on defining racism as a problematic way of thinking. When being a conscious racist became a high moral crime, people were disinclined to admit they internalized the centuries-old resentments and condescending views towards POC. Further exacerbating this problem is the fact that our national culture has been very slow to integrate the idea of unconscious racism into our collective conversations. As a result, many whites now believe that as long as they do not engage in conscious bigotry, they are completely free of racism. Moreover, they can also safely disregard any moral obligation for racial disparities due to current and historical racism.

> The anti-racism advocate must help the racism skeptic see that racism is more nuanced than the old-fashioned bigotry. The best way to do this...[is] by owning up to the fact that the ally themselves sometimes is affected by these biases.

The result is that huge proportions of the white population do not care that on virtually all measures of opportunity and well-being – life expectancy, having a good public school and adequate health care, the chance that they will not grow up near a source of significant pollution– the prospects facing a newborn of color are predictably much worse hat of a white newborn. It is not clear whether most white folks know s true, but it is clear they do not see these racially disparate prospects newborns as a national problem.

This sense of disconnect from the moral problem of racial disparities – which too frequently takes the form of refusing to address racial problems - creates a complex challenge for white allies. The anti-racism advocate must help the racism skeptic see that racism is more nuanced than old-fashioned bigotry. The best way to do this is to normalize the experience of having biased beliefs and to do so by owning up to the fact that the ally themselves sometimes is affected by these biases. It is important to reduce the stigma of having these views, since virtually everyone (including POC) has been affected to some extent by societal stereotypes. The ally must convey that no one is completely innocent, including themselves.

At the same time, the ally cannot go too far in removing the moral significance of these views. The ally must try to get the skeptic to understand that the pervasiveness of these views is linked to ongoing racial disparities in society that have deep practical and moral implications. And the ally must thread this needle while working around the ingrained tendency of racism skeptics to look away from these problems, to blame POC for their overall condition, and to see any analysis that looks unflinchingly at racism as attempts to leverage white guilt.

Your task as an ally is to invite your skeptic – over multiple conversations over a period of time – to understand several points:

- There are a number of patterns of human behavior that have some universal dimensions, but within the American racial context they are enacted in a way that reinforces racial disparities, systematically disadvantage people of color, and reinforce very old patterns of unfairness.
- It is possible to participate in these patterns without conscious intent and without being an evil person.
- These disparities result in newborns of some racial groups having demonstrably better chances at healthy long lives than others. Many have not changed much since slavery. Everyone can decide

for themselves about moral implications for contributing, even unintentionally, in a system that perpetuates disparities with their origins in a clearly immoral social system.

- These disparities perpetuate themselves because the society has created a narrative among most whites that they are not a function of current and historical racism, but rather due to inherent inferiority in people of color themselves.
- Even if the behavior of people of color were partially responsible for the disparities they experience (and this is highly questionable),historical and current racism also plays a role.
- While no single individual or institution has the power to completely undo societal racism and the disparities caused by it, everyone can take some steps towards progress on these issues. At a minimum, everyone can work to undermine the narrative that completely blames people of color for the disparities in well-being that they experience.

The approach of interacting with racism skeptics suggested in the foregoing primer is very similar to the RACE Method in Part Two; however there is an important modification. The modules previously discussed focus on how you can respond in the moment to an unexpected comment by a racism skeptic that is racially-problematic. This primer envisions that you will initiate conversations about racial issues, with the intention of doing some coaching over a period of time.

To take someone through this curriculum, you need to not only invite the skeptic into the topic. You must be able to convey anecdotes that raise thorny racial issues, and do so in a way that stimulates their interest in staying with the topic. The inner work needed for using this primer is very similar to the modules. It is important to have your own anecdotes together, so you can engage in mutual storytelling. One difference is that, instead of leading with curiosity about the skeptic's perspective, you are usually leading with vulnerability and exposure of your past or on-going foibles. **It is important that you make it safe for the skeptic to admit their connection to unfortunate racial dynamics that they might be disinclined to admit to themselves or others.**

This primer presents ideas in a general sequence that is likely to be most effective in slowly coaching a skeptic up a ladder of understanding. The approach of this workbook is to not offer extensive academic treatises about each of the points of the primer, though the text will point you to resources where you can do more learning. Each concept will be briefly described under the assumption that this is enough for you to engage a skeptic. Several points will be reviewed that are important to keep in mind as you prepare conversational strategies. These points include:

Why the Concept is Important for Skeptics to Understand – Since your skeptic's resistance may be very entrenched, remind yourself of why it is useful to spend your energy to get them to understand this point.

How the Concept Manifests in Everyday Life – Often, showing the skeptic that the concept has relevance outside the race context can reduce their resistance to applying it to the racial context. For many of the concepts, it will be useful to have one personal example of the concept outside of the racial context, and one personal example of how it applies when race is involved.

Why This Concept Can Be Difficult To Clearly Recognize – Remembering the ways the concept can stay hidden may be important when your patience with your skeptic grows thin. In addition, reminding the skeptic that the phenomenon is often camouflaged can help them stay in the hunt for it, especially if they trust you.

Why Skeptics Resist and/or What Resistance Looks Like – It is important to be prepared for the way resistance can emerge so that you stay centered and not overly frustrated.

Some Conversational Strategies – For most of the concepts, we provide more than one conversational sequence with a reasonable chance of helping a skeptic warm to the idea that racism is real and worthy of attention. The hope is that you will very deliberately experiment with different strategies, reflect on the results to improve your own practice, and report back to the White Ally Toolkit (via our Facebook page or our website), so that the ally community can benefit from what you have learned.

Individual Reflection Questions – If you are going to get a skeptic to own up to their casual participation in societal racism, it is vital that you do this too, so that they know it's safe. Answering these reflection questions yourself is a vital preparation to make such in invitation.

Discussion Suggestions for a Group – While most users of this workbook will be reading it as part of their personal ally practice, we strongly encourage people to be a part of in-person or online communities of people who have decided that influencing skeptics is a part of their anti-racism ally work. These suggestions may help you create processes that will deepen reflection and commitment to trying these techniques.

Sources of Additional Data – For most items in the primer, we hope you jump right in and start working with skeptics after you do some reflection and strategizing. Reading lists should not be excuses for procrastination! But for those who want to learn more about the topic, we provide a few resources.

RACIAL ISSUES – THE COLLECTIVE CONCEPTS

OTHERING

WHAT IT IS

- Othering refers to the tendency by humans to consciously or semi-consciously conceptualize those in other social groups as being significantly different from those in their own group and thus deserving of different treatment.
- This tendency is widespread and is related to humans' deeply embedded tribal behavior.

WHY IT IS IMPORTANT

Some argue that othering is the fundamental behavior that drives not only racism, but many other isms that involve oppression of some groups (sexism, homophobia, xenophobia, etc.).

HOW IT MANIFESTS

Outside The Racial Context

- Group competitions in artificial settings
- Distrust of people from other neighborhoods, cities, or regions
- Intense rivalries between sports teams and their fans
- Conflicts between immigrants based on their regions of origin
- Exaggerated small differences between groups
- Homophobia: hatred of sexual minorities

In The Context Of Race/Ethnicity

- Seeing people of other groups as more criminally minded, less intelligent, etc.
- Seeing people from other groups as more cunning, more docile, or smarter

- Xenophobia: hatred of people from other nations
- Tribal conflicts around the world
- Ethnic cleansing
- Ethnic cleansing; genocide
- Slavery

WHY IT IS HARD TO SEE

- It's a natural phenomenon that happens in a multiplicity of ways.
- Othering outside of the racial context is easier to see, and often easier for people to admit.
- Being a "racist" has become a significant moral crime, so people do not want to admit they do othering by race, even infrequently and subtly.
- When people admit they do othering in the racial context, they are often shamed instead of appreciated for their honesty.

PREPARING FOR RESISTANCE FROM SKEPTICS

Here are some of the things said by skeptics who are resistant to acknowledging othering on the basis of race:

- "Divisions between groups is the natural order of things."
- "You believe in cultural differences, right? Some cultures just have more problems than others."
- "People have always been loyal to their group, and this is OK."
- "What happens in the U.S. is no worse than other places, and is arguably better than most."
- "The best way to avoid doing this is to decide that I don't see differences. We are supposed to be colorblind anyway, right?"

REFLECTION QUESTIONS

1. If you have one, describe an experience where out of loyalty to a group you are in (not race based) you found yourself excessively othering

people in a different group? (Examples might be people in other school neighborhoods or fraternal organizations).What happens for you emotionally when you find yourself othering people? Are there situations where this bothers you, or does not bother you? What affects your emotions about it? How do you think your emotional reaction affects your ability to spot your own behavior about this?

2. If you have one, describe an experience where you observed someone excessively othering people from a different group (not necessarily because of race) because of circumstances and/or their loyalty to their own group.
3. What did adults teach you about people from other groups? What were the verbal and non-verbal messages you got about how different groups – especially racial but perhaps others - were fundamentally similar? What were the verbal and non-verbal messages you got about how different groups were, in fact, rather different?
4. If you can remember an early experience where you acted on the belief that POC were different, describe it.
5. What was a formative experience that reflected you coming to your own conclusions about group similarities and/or differences?
6. Have you ever observed a situation where a POC was othering someone of a different racial/ethnic group? If so, how do you explain why this was happening?
7. Describe an experience in the past few years where you mentally othered a POC, even if you did not mean to do so, or even if the effect on your behavior was slight/not discernible.

SOME CONVERSATIONAL STRATEGIES

Your primary objective is to get the skeptic to understand/admit they are subject to sometimes regarding POC as other, even if they only do this now and then. The primary approach is to admit that you sometimes do this and that doing this does not make you a horrible person. However, you are also not trying to conceptualize othering as a positive behavior. Your primary messages are:

- Othering is a natural human phenomenon that is sometimes harmless (sports teams) and is often taken too far (gangs, war).
- Othering on the basis of race is unambiguously bad.
- Even good people who are taught to not think of POC as other are subject to doing this now and then.

Strategy 1: Position othering as a common human behavior that can sometimes go awry. After establishing that, pivot to how good people sometimes do this by race.

1. Discuss a time when you witnessed a person othering another group (not based on race) in a way that went too far.
2. Discuss a situation where group loyalty (not based on race) caused you to make inaccurate/unnecessary conclusions about other groups.
3. Ask them if they have ever done something similar, out of feelings of intense group loyalty.
4. If appropriate, frame othering as a natural tendency that can be fun in the right proportion (e.g. sporting rivalries), but also destructive if taken too far.
5. Talk briefly about a time a long ago when you mentally othered a POC. If necessary, blame your upbringing.
6. Talk briefly about a time when you othered a POC as an adult. If necessary, blame media portrayals, bad experiences, or other plausible causes. Don't position the behavior as showing bad character.
7. See if they are willing to own up to ever having othered a POC in the distant past, then in the more recent past.
8. As needed, explore their sense of why this happened, including their upbringing.
9. If you need to further assuage their defensiveness – briefly discuss a time when you observed a POC doing this to a white person, or another person who they considered different.

Note: the risk of this strategy is that it may take too long for people who do not have the patience to follow an extensive through line with one topic.

Strategy 2: Position othering by race as a behavior that most people were taught by those who loved them.

1. Discuss what you were taught about other racial groups by your parents or by other early influences. Tell at least one story of being influenced to look at POC as other.
2. Explore any influences they may have had to seeing POC as other.
3. Discuss other circumstances you have seen where young people (especially whites) were influenced to see groups as other. Do not frame this in conservative/liberal terms, especially if the skeptic is conservative. If you have one, tell an example of an othering by a white person whom you know was liberal, and work that fact in the anecdote in a way that doesn't seem obtrusive.
4. Discuss how you see othering behavior in your own subtle thoughts, even if these thoughts seem to rarely affect your behavior.
5. Discuss how you see othering behavior by other people, especially other white people.
6. Explore whether they can remember any time, even long ago, when they engaged in othering, either in their minds or in their actions.

Consider whether it is useful to discuss whatever judgments you made about yourself when you have othered people. If you bring up your negative self-judgment, frame these judgments as impeding you from being honest with yourself about what you are actually doing. (For more ideas about this, see the discussion about Shame in the Odds and Ends section.)

Strategy 3: Start with racial othering by leveraging their likely belief in "reverse racism"

1. Optional: Frame the conversation as about unfortunate divisions in the country.
2. Discuss a time when you observed a person of color othering someone.
3. Invite them to discuss if they have ever seen something like this.
4. Frame the behavior in a universal human context.
5. Discuss a time when you did this to a person of color a long time ago.
6. Discuss a time when you othered a person of color more recently.
7. Invite them to describe a time when they have looked at a person of color as other.
8. Lightly touch on the fact that even though othering is a general tendency for all groups, the impact on all groups is not the same. (Don't hammer too much on this point...you can come back to issues of relative impact at a later time. The critical task is to admit that you are subject to othering by race, and to get them to admit that they are too).

UNCONSCIOUS BIAS

WHAT IT IS

- The automatic and unintentional associations – often negative – that people make between groups of people and sets of ideas.
- These biases often exist below the awareness of the person who has the bias.
- In many cases, these biases run counter to the conscious values the person has. For instance, many white people deeply committed to racial justice still have unconscious biases against people of color.

> Put simply, unconscious bias creates uncertainty around any person's claim that they are not biased, and attribution error casts doubt on any person's assertion that someone else has bias.

- One illustration of the way these biases work unintentionally is that research has shown that substantial proportions of people of color have an unconscious bias against their own racial group.

The phenomena of unconscious bias and othering are very closely related, and are arguably two aspects of the same behavior. To the extent there is a difference, it is the degree we are aware of how our minds are working. For the sake of moving the skeptic up a ladder of understanding, the unconscious bias idea is more important. If you can get a skeptic to acknowledge its reality, unconscious bias provides a way for the skeptic to lessen their focus on conscious intent. This focus blocks a good deal of white people's understanding about how modern racism works.

WHY IT IS IMPORTANT

- Many white people believe that if they are not consciously biased, they cannot be part of the societal problem of racism.

- Helping skeptics see that you and they are both subject to being unconsciously racist helps combat the "Racism is not my problem" perspective.
- To deepen one's understanding of racism, it is important to see that racial bias can be hidden from the person who has it while being apparent to observers.
- Helping skeptics see that POC are subject to unconscious bias all the time can help undermine the idea that racism is all in the past and that claims of racism are cynical and self-interested.

HOW IT MANIFESTS:

There is very good documentation about the ways that unconscious bias shows up in behavior toward POC. It is useful to be able to repeat stories about what you have observed or have been told by people you trust. Stories from the perspective of POC are powerful, but when talking to skeptics, stories from other white people admitting to being affected by unconscious bias may be more impactful. Examples include:

- Subtle safety based behaviors, such as: crossing the street, locking car doors, clutching purses in the presence of a POC.
- Making less eye contact and smiling less.
- Having lower expectations or being surprised that people of color are competent or accomplished.
- Giving people of color less favorable evaluations for jobs or during employment.
- Just having the feeling that someone of color "would not fit in."
- Providing lower quality customer service to people of color in restaurants, health care facilities, retail establishments, and so on.

WHY IT IS HARD TO SEE

- By its nature, unconscious bias is very difficult for the person with the bias to see. It is also difficult for observers to see with complete reliability. (One of the reasons scientists know it exists is it is possible to perform studies looking at large numbers and observe the effect of race on a group of people, even though each individual in a group might honestly claim to not be affected by race).

- The narrative that "racism = unabashed bigotry" is deeply ingrained in American culture. Many think in very "yes or no" terms, and unconscious bias adds an additional gray area that may challenge some people's preferred way of categorizing with ideas.

PREPARING FOR RESISTANCE FROM SKEPTICS

Some reasons that skeptics will resist:

- Acknowledging that unconscious racism exists can make skeptics fear they open the door for an infinite number of claims of racism, some of which are inaccurate or even cynical.
- Unconscious bias creates self-doubt and this is difficult for people who dislike ambiguity, which many conservatives do.
- Admitting that pervasive unconscious bias against POC exists counters the idea that today's white people as a group are innocent of America's historic racism problem.

REFLECTION QUESTIONS

1. Was there a time when you did not think that unconscious racial bias was something you might have? If you can remember it, describe a period of your life or an incident when you were denying that you had any bias?
2. If you had an eye opening experience in realizing that unconscious bias was real, jot some notes below.
3. If you have had an experience where you realized that you were subject to unconscious bias by others, jot some notes about this below.
4. If you have heard a story from a person of color that you trust (not necessarily someone you know personally) discussing the way that unconscious bias by whites affects them, jot a few notes about this experience as well as how you felt when you first heard it.
5. If you have taken the Implicit Association Test[1], jot down your experience of taking the test and absorbing the results.

1 https://implicit.harvard.edu/implicit/

SOME CONVERSATIONAL STRATEGIES

Strategy 1. Start by exploring how skeptics might have faced unconscious bias against them.

1. Discuss some quality you have that makes you sometimes subject to bias.
2. Identify a quality they have that may make them subject to unconscious bias, e.g. gender, weight, strong accent, disability, etc.
3. Try to get them to admit that other people's biases about them is something they have to work around.
4. Discuss a way that you are subject to occasional bias because of some quality (be careful of doing this before getting them to admit they are sometimes victims of bias. You may be forced to spend conversational energy trying to convince them that you are a victim).
5. If there is some shared quality that makes both of you subject to bias, so much the better!
6. Turn the concept around and raise the topic of biases that either of you might have. Discuss one that is not based on race. After telling an anecdote where you illustrate doing this, ask them if they ever noticed they have a bias about some group, even if was only a passing thought.

Strategy 2: Start by owning up to racial bias you have felt (this is basically starting at step 6 above).

1. Talk about your subtle biases based on race in the past based on upbringing or circumstances.
2. After positioning having unconscious bias as a forgivable act, ask if your skeptic can admit to ever noticing themselves having a unconscious racial biases at some point in the past.
3. If you have one, tell your story about how you came to see a bias you previously did not think that you did.
4. Based on your own experiences of what you learned from other white allies, invite them to consider the possibility they sometimes still have biases that affect them.

Strategy 3: Start with the fact that a person of color can have bias against their own group, and pivot to how bias affects you and them.

1. Relate evidence that POC sometimes have biases against their own group. Some evidence:
   - Doll studies, such as done by Kenneth Clarke in the 1950's[2] and CNN in 2010.[3]
   - Results from Implicit Association Test (some studies have found that 28% of blacks have an unconscious preference for whites over blacks).[4]
2. Discuss how seeing this evidence gives you the courage to look at yourself.
3. Discuss your journey to realize that you were not free of bias; if possible, include negative ideas about POC you were exposed to in childhood.
4. Invite them to consider how bias might affect them; ground it in their upbringing if necessary.

Strategy 4: Have them take the Implicit Association Test.

The Implicit Association Test (IAT) is a widely used instrument for measuring unconscious bias. It can be done online in a few minutes. There are versions of the instrument that focus on race, gender, disability, and many other dimensions of identity. As a white ally, you should complete the instrument for your own reflection, whether or not you make discussing your experience of the instrument part of your strategies with racism skeptics.

1. Invite the skeptic to take the IAT, either in your presence or not.
2. Brush up on the evidence that the IAT is widely accepted as valid[5],

---

2 New York Times, May 7, 2014
3 http://www.cnn.com/2010/US/05/13/doll.study/index.html
4 http://www.pewsocialtrends.org/2015/08/19/exploring-racial-bias-among-biracial-and-single-race-adults-the-iat/
5 http://www.washingtonpost.com/wp-dyn/articles/A27067-2005Jan21.html

though it does have its critics.[6]

3. Be prepared for the possibility that they will want to reject the results.
4. Talk about your reaction to your own results, especially those that reflect an inclination to deny or reject the results.
5. Discuss the skeptic's experience of the IAT. Bring to bear as much empathy as possible if they are prone to rejecting or otherwise minimizing the results.

No matter which strategy you choose:

- At some point, convey that there is scientific consensus that the best way to fight bias is to admit it and work actively against it.[7] Frame this as ironic, if helpful.
- Emphasize that we do not have to feel guilty for having bias, but must be morally accountable for doing something about it.

6 https://www.chronicle.com/article/Can-We-Really-Measure-Implicit/238807
7 https://www.psychologytoday.com/us/blog/sound-science-sound-policy/201501/overcoming-implicit-bias-and-racial-anxiety

ATTRIBUTION ERROR

WHAT IT IS

Attribution error concerns the inherent difficulty that people face in trying to understand other people's actions and reasons for them. The term most commonly refers to the tendency to explain their behavior by implicating their character, instead of the circumstances they are facing. By contrast, when explaining their own behavior, people much more frequently refer to situational factors as driving forces. Sometimes the term refers to the fact that people in disadvantaged groups have a very difficult time knowing if they are being treated poorly because of their group status.

WHY IT IS IMPORTANT

If you can get a skeptic to understand the concept (its complexity may make this difficult in some cases), you can invite them away from the view that people overly claim racism because they are cynically "playing the race card." Instead, you can help them see that attribution error may play a role in such claims. The concept also potentially highlights their own error about how others are playing the race card. The concept also can be an on-ramp to discuss the way that whites sometimes make assessments about POC that conform with stereotypes (e.g. lazy, unintelligent, criminally-minded, etc.)

HOW IT MANIFESTS

- People of color thinking that a white person's behavior is a function of their bias, when their behavior is actually related to the situation they are confronting.
- White people thinking that a person of color's behavior is a function of some negative trait about them when it is actually related to the situation they are confronting (like racism that is invisible to most white people).

PREPARING FOR RESISTANCE FROM SKEPTICS:

This may be a challenge for people who are not oriented toward abstract thinking. It demands that they do the mental gymnastics of looking at the same situation from different points of view.

Note: One way to potentially introduce this concept and reduce initial resistance by the skeptic, is to raise the possibility that it applies to accusations that POC make about racism. After the skeptic integrates the concept, you can later raise how it applies to whites generally and themselves.

REFLECTION QUESTIONS

1. Describe an experience you have had that is primarily NOT race related where attribution error might have been affecting a conclusion someone made about you (or that you made about someone else).It's best if the story has a very vivid reveal moment, so that it is easy to see that the person making the conclusion simply overlooked some situation-specific factors that really mattered.
2. Describe an experience you had (or know of) that does involve race (not accusations of racism) where attribution error was very likely playing a role. After remembering the basic core of the story, practice framing the key dynamics in light of attribution error.
3. Describe a situation where a person (best if it's a white person) was suspected of or accused of having a racially prejudiced intent and you thought this was more likely wrong than right. Practice telling the story in a way that leads to a takeaway about attribution error.

SOME CONVERSATIONAL STRATEGIES

A core decision that you have to sort out is: At what point do you point directly at this concept and its high falutin name and accompanying complexity? If your skeptic is a conceptual thinker, presenting attribution error as a concept early in the conversation may be intriguing; it will still be important to leverage your and their experiences to explore the concept. If the skeptic tends toward concrete thinking, it may be useful to focus on experiences first.

Strategy 1: Introduce a non-racial experience involving attribution error, then pivot to a racial situation.

1. Discuss a personal experience not related to race where attribution error affected you (either because you came to bad conclusions or someone came to bad conclusions about you);

2. Explain the concept of attribution error;
3. Invite them to tell you an experience where attribution error affected them – in either direction;
4. Reinforce that this is a basic and common human error relevant to many circumstances;
5. Recall a situation where you thought attribution error was involved in someone's suspicions/accusation (could be a POC or a white person) that a white person was operating on racially biased motivations;
6. Explore if they have ever seen a situation like this and have them tell you about it;
7. Link the accusations to attribution error;
8. If they make comments suggesting that accusations of racism are a tendency of people of color, have a conversation about how attribution error may be influencing the skeptic's own perspective on this.

Strategy 2: Start from a situation involving a potentially inaccurate assertion of racism.

Same as Strategy 1, except start at step 5

Strategy 3: Start with a case when a racial stereotype appeared to affect a person of color.

1. Discuss a situation where a white person explained a person of color's behavior with a racialized explanation that you thought was inappropriate. Include how you felt in the moment.
2. Explain attribution error and how learning about it gave you more empathy for the white person in the situation.
3. If you have any examples, share a story about you explaining a POC's behavior in a way that reflected attribution error. (Depending on the emotional import of these stories, it may be more effective to do this step before #1 and 2).
4. Invite them to share an experience of making a negative assessment related to race where, in retrospect, they see that attribution error might have been at work.

5. Remind them that attribution error should make us more compassionate toward people who make false conclusions, as well as more humble about conclusions that we draw.
6. Shift the focus to attributions about racism by relating an experience where someone attributed a racist motivation in a way that you thought might have been inappropriate.
7. Explore a situation where someone made a claim of racist motivation that they thought was likely inappropriate.

Note: There is a very important relationship between unconscious bias and attribution error

There is an interesting interaction between unconscious bias and attribution error. The reality of unconscious bias means that humans are subject to acting in ways that reflects motivations they are not aware of. On the other hand, attribution error means they often attribute motivations about other people's behavior to factors about them (such as unconscious bias) in a way that might be inaccurate. Put simply, unconscious bias creates uncertainty around any person's claim that they are not biased, and attribution error casts doubt on any person's assertion that someone else has bias. **There is no clean way out of this knot of ambiguity.** If people are disagreeing about the role that bias plays in a situation, they will likely need to rely on interpersonal dialogue and some measure of humility to make progress toward a shared understanding.

This knot of ambiguity is made more complicated by the fear that many white people have that POC are often judging them as a bigot. This concern is the next topic, which is called racial anxiety.

RACIAL ANXIETY

WHAT IT IS

- Racial anxiety is the fear that someone will make a negative assessment of their character based on race.
- This is primarily thought of in cross-racial encounters, though this might be changing as progressives and conservative whites are increasingly at loggerheads around racial issues.
- For people of color, racial anxiety is a centuries-old problem of worrying that whites might feel about them negatively.
- For whites, this issue has only been around for a few decades; specifically, it is the worry that a person of color will think that they are a racist.

WHY IT IS IMPORTANT

- Many white people have a subtle level of nervousness in encounters with people of color. Sometimes, this nervousness – which can exist below conscious awareness – can cause the white person to make a variety of negative assessments of their counterparts or of the encounter.
- Racial anxiety can also cause people to make small choices that effectively lower the probability of having encounters across racial lines. By naming racial anxiety as a general phenomenon that can affect everyone, it may be easier for your skeptic to be honest with themselves about what happens for them in cross-racial encounters.
- Many white people hold racial grievances, and feel that "white people have racial problems too." By naming a commonly held feeling – even though you should not primarily blame people of color for this – you are meeting the skeptic with the sensibility they may already have.

HOW IT MANIFESTS

Interestingly, racial anxiety produces some of the same behavioral responses as when people are actually racially biased, such as

- Less eye contact
- Less smiling or laughing
- Increased nervousness and fidgeting
- Shorter verbal responses and less willingness to verbally engage

Racial anxiety often causes white people to come away from an encounter with a person of color with a feeling they were being judged as racist, even if this was not actually true.

WHY AND HOW SKEPTICS RESIST

Since POC often do think that whites harbor conscious or unconscious racist feelings toward them, the supposition that this is happening is not always wrong. As a result, skeptics may fall back on an "It's not me, it's them," point of view.

ON LANGUAGE

Many people, especially men, have a strong resistance to the idea that they have anything that might be labeled "anxiety." If you think this applies to one of the skeptics you are working with, you might use a different word, like "racial doubt" or "racist concern". The core point is that this feeling among white people may have nothing to do with the actual thoughts of POC in a particular situation.

REFLECTION QUESTIONS

1. Jot some notes down about an experience where you were nervous about what someone (not in a position of power over you) thought about you that had nothing to do with race. If possible, choose an experience where you subsequently received strong confirmation that most or all of your fears that you had were unwarranted.
2. Jot some notes down about a time you remember worrying about being perceived as racist by people of color. Group experiences are OK, but one-on-one or very small group experiences will likely be more effective. If you have multiple possibilities, write them all down. Take note of which stories will be most compelling, either because your anxiety level was high, your discovery that your anxiety was misplaced was very clear, or for some other reason.

3. If you have ever had a conversation with other white folks about feeling nervous about being perceived as racist by people of color, recall one or two of those experiences here. As above, stories where people discuss one-on-one encounters are usually better, since large group settings have different dynamics.
4. If you have ever had a person of color tell you about reassuring a white person that they were not judging them, recall some elements of that conversation.

SOME CONVERSATIONAL STRATEGIES

Your overall goal is to get the skeptic to admit they are subject to feeling a bit of racial anxiety. While you want them to be as honest as possible about how often this affects them, an admission that they have ever had this feeling means they concede that white people might experience this even more frequently. Thus, racial anxiety becomes part of your shared frame of analysis about racial dynamics.

Strategy 1: Start with racial anxiety and a time when you felt it

This strategy can work if you and the skeptic already have a shared understanding that unnecessary anxieties sometimes affect human interaction.

1. Discuss a time when you felt racial anxiety yourself.
2. If you can remember one, share an experience of conversation with other whites over being nervous about being perceived as racist.
3. At this point, you have provided a gradual on-ramp to them admitting to sometimes having racial anxiety. Invite the skeptic to share a time when they felt nervous because of how they might be judged as racist.
4. As they tell the story, try to get them to recall how their behavior might have been different than if they did not feel that anxiety.
5. If the two of you have a shared understanding that there are highly prejudiced white people in the world, discuss how some behaviors caused by racial anxiety are similar to what happens when overt racists do not want to connect with people of color for that reason. If your previous conversations have not established that there are

otherwise good people who have racial prejudices, you may want to skip this step. (The issue of highly racially prejudiced people will be directly dealt with later in this sequence.)

6. Discuss possible strategies for people to connect in the face of all of these swirling feelings.

Strategy 2: Start with interpersonal anxiety about being judged (not about race), then pivot toward a racial situation. This is a longer on-ramp to the conversation, and may be appropriate when there is no shared understanding that anxiety is a common factor in human interaction.

1. Discuss a time when you were nervous, not related to race, about how someone felt about you and later discovered your anxieties turned out to be mostly unfounded. (If you know a situation like this involving someone else, that is OK.) The key point is that the subject of the story was making unfounded or significantly overblown judgments of others in the story.
2. Explore whether this has ever happened to them and invite them to share this experience.
3. Pause for a moment to focus your alignment on the fact that anxieties, sometimes unfounded, can make interactions more difficult.
4. After you have established that non-racial anxiety can disrupt interactions, discuss a time when you felt racial anxiety yourself.
5. Continue with steps #1 through 6 from Strategy 1.

UNEARNED RACIAL ADVANTAGE (COMMONLY CALLED WHITE PRIVILEGE)

WHAT IT IS

- **Unearned racial advantage is the state of enjoying benefits from being part of a group that is considered "normal" or even superior in one, some, or many aspects of life.**
- **Alternate Definition:** The state of not being part of a group that is frequently mistreated by institutions and individuals. Also, not experiencing frequent race-based mistreatment across a number of life dimensions, such as employment, health care, and/or education.

WHY IT IS IMPORTANT

- Many have argued that most white people have a deeply ambivalent relationship to the idea that whiteness carries advantages. People are highly resistant to acknowledging this, even though a minuscule proportion of whites would say they would rather be non-white.
- The lack of clarity about whether there are advantages to being white makes it easier to deny that racism causes unfairness to people of color and thereby hurts society.
- If one acknowledges that whiteness has unearned advantages, it is more difficult to also maintain that racism is over.

HOW IT MANIFESTS

- Not accepting that unearned racial advantages overwhelmingly benefits whites enables whites to cultivate racial grievances.
- Denying unearned racial advantage keeps white people from seeing American society as it actually functions and lowers empathy towards people of color.
- Denial of this concept tends to support a diminished support for efforts to improve racial equity.

WHY AND HOW SKEPTICS RESIST

Common strategies of resistance:

- Focusing on how hard they and other whites have had to work
- Shifting attention to POC who have had economic advantages
- Shifting attention to POC who defied the odds
- Avoiding the discussion of racism
- Shifting attention to white people who have more advantages than the skeptic does, based on class status
- Overemphasizing the rare cases when a POC has a racial advantage

While this project does not categorically discourage use of the words "white privilege" with racism skeptics, it is worth noting that many workshop participants have told us that this word often triggers people and tends to make conversation about the phenomenon more difficult.

Previous parts of this primer have suggested that you consider raising concepts in a non-race based way, get the skeptic's buy in, and then apply the concept to racial situations. You should consider this approach here as well. Specifically, consider framing unearned racial advantage as something that can theoretically affect any group. (For example, tall black men benefit from positive assumptions when they are near a basketball pick-up game, regardless of their actual level of skill.) Once you establish unearned racial advantage as a generalizable phenomenon, you can shift the discussion to examine how this concept applies to various groups, and the relative impact on these groups.

ON LANGUAGE

Do not get stuck on calling this phenomenon "white privilege" because:

- Some people will resist the word "privilege" because this idea does not fit their narrative for themselves
- Some people will resist the word "white" because they will associate this word with old fashioned bigotry

If you don't like the phrase "unearned racial advantage", other options include:

- White advantage, or advantages to being white
- Racial privilege
- White racial advantage
- Racial "leg up"

While this project does not categorically discourage use of the words "white privilege" with racism skeptics, it is worth noting that many workshop participants have told us it triggers people and tends to make conversation about the phenomenon more difficult.[8] We encourage you to experiment with terminology. Your focus should be on upgrading the skeptic's conceptualization about how race works in society, not their vocabulary.

REFLECTION QUESTIONS

1. If you can think of a story that you have heard about a person of color having an unearned racial advantage, jot notes about the story here.

---

8 "I use those terms: white supremacy, racism, white privilege – and what I have found is that if you use those terms, before other person knows what you mean, it breaks down communication. Because I know what I mean but they don't know what I mean. For instance, if you use the term white privilege, they say "You are more privileged than I am. What do you mean? I don't have white privilege!" They don't understand what you are talking about. Same thing with racism. I have to do better at breaking myself of it, but I have to stop using terms where I know what I mean but they don't what I mean. It breaks down communication." – Participant in White Ally Toolkit Workshop, Detroit

2. What was your most powerful memory of hearing experiences from a person of color that made it clear to you that white privilege was a real thing?
3. What are the things you don't have to worry about because you are white that you can talk about in the most compelling way?
4. Were there any particularly powerful, direct experiences that brought home to you the advantages of being white?
5. Before you became aware of white privilege, what were your strongest arguments about why you were NOT privileged?

SOME CONVERSATIONAL STRATEGIES

Strategy 1: Pivot from the idea that unearned racial advantage is a general concept that can apply to people of color sometimes. (This only works if you have 1-2 stories like this)

1. Discuss a story you have heard about a POC benefiting from positive assumptions in a way that denotes racial advantage in a specific domain.
2. Confirm that the skeptic agrees that they see the story as connoting unearned racial advantage.
3. Tell a story from your own experience about when you think you experienced unearned advantage from being white. (It's best if the story involves receiving real benefits, instead of just your lack of worry about how others will treat you.)
4. Ask if they have ever experienced a situation where they thought that they had an advantage because they were white.
5. After getting agreement that unearned racial advantage exists and can cut different ways at different times, have a conversation about the relative magnitude and significance of how racial advantage for different groups plays out for society and for individuals. (For example, a black person assumed to be a good athlete has some impact in specific settings, while a white person assumed to be trustworthy has an arguably bigger impact in many more settings.) It is useful to have done some thinking about this beforehand, so that you are not struggling for points during the conversation.

6. If you had an emotional reaction when you first accepted the idea of white privilege, discuss this reaction. If it seems like it will advance your connection, see if the skeptic has any feelings about the idea that they have built-in advantages over POC.

Strategy 2: Pivot from your own experiences.

1. Consider referencing the previous conversations on subjects of this primer that connote the advantages of being white. For instance, worrying about being considered racist, while certainly a problem, is not as bad as worrying about being considered inferior.
2. If you can be articulate and believable about it, discuss aspects of unearned racial advantage that concern not having to worry about common difficulties (e.g. mistreatment by police, discrimination in retail). The key for this to work in the conversation is that you have actually experienced these advantages on an emotional level, and you are not just reading from a liberal script.
3. Expand the view from "being white means less worry" to the question of whether being white is just easier overall.
4. Discuss 1-2 examples that are vivid for you that illustrate benefiting from white racial advantage.
5. Explore whether the skeptic ever feels that being white is an advantage. If they are willing to admit it, invite them to share one specific story that illustrates this. Unless you are completely confident that it will help the conversation, do NOT suggest that they have any obligation to do anything about this. By adding a moral obligation to the admission that being white is easier, you make this admission more difficult. Trust that you can return to the moral implications in a later conversation.
6. If they resist acknowledging how being white has advantages in many circumstances, try this thought experiment: Have them imagine themselves as a soul about to enter two possible just-created embryos, one white and one black. Have them imagine that the two embryos are from families with the same economic background. Ask them how they would make a decision about which embryo they would choose

to house their soul for a lifetime. You might run the experiment multiple times with different birth years. You may need to review the concepts from previous conversations if it is not obvious to the skeptic that being white has many advantages. Feel free to express your perspective and the reasons why you would make the choice you would make. Do not approach the conversation as if they are categorically wrong. Be sure to participate with an attitude of inquiry and exploration if you want them to do the same.

7. Explore whether any part of them resists or does not like the idea that they benefit from being white. Again, if you remember when part of you resisted this admission, bring up this experience.
8. Discuss how you have come to terms with white racial advantage. Be careful to NOT convey that the only way to effectively respond to the reality of white advantage is to be as committed as you are to racial equity. Instead, provide 2-3 small things that you do or have done. Remember, your goal is to make it easy to admit that there are advantages to being white; conveying a sense of significant moral obligations may make it harder for them to be honest about having these advantages.
9. Keep in mind, your goal is to not create a full-fledged convert, but rather someone who is willing to be a little open to something they have denied, and who might consider small steps to redress the unfairness they now see.

RACIAL THREAT

WHAT IT IS

Racial threat is the discomfort that individuals and groups sometimes feel when they observe developments that they think threaten to cause a decline in the political power, social status, prestige, and/or advantages of their racial group.

WHY IT IS IMPORTANT

- Racial threat has always been part of the interaction between racial groups, with white populations responding by taking steps to protect their group power.
- Arguably, racial threat is a dominant factor in how white populations have dealt with non-white populations since colonization.
- Moreover, there is good research that concludes the popularity of Donald Trump is a reflection of the widespread feeling of racial threat among white people.[9]
- Racial threat can affect people of color, too. For instance, there has been significant angst in the black community in Detroit, Washington DC, Brooklyn, and other places about gentrification and losses in economic and political power.
- Pointing out racial threat as a phenomenon that other groups sometimes experience may make it easier for a skeptic to believe that it affects white populations.

HOW IT MANIFESTS

- People who experience racial threat often feel heightened resentment toward people from other groups, regardless of whether those individuals have anything to do with this perceived potential loss of group status.
- In extreme circumstances, these feelings can results in violent hate crimes, riots, and/or mob attacks.

---

9 https://www.vox.com/identities/2017/12/15/16781222/trump-racism-economic-anxiety-study

- These feelings can also result in large-scale group behavior, such as mass actions to suppress groups or retain certain perceived benefits. This may include enacting laws or policies or electing public officials so that the relevant branch of government protects one group's perceived status.

WHY AND HOW SKEPTICS RESIST

- Unless they are extreme racists, white skeptics are not used to thinking of themselves as part of a racial group that has self-perceived group interests.
- The idea of white people having group interests that they sometimes defend or pursue has echoes of an extremely uncomfortable racial history.
- To defend against feeling connected to this long history of group suppression, skeptics are likely to have some resistance to admitting these inklings.

SOME CONVERSATIONAL STRATEGIES

Racial threat may be a very scary strategy for a skeptic to contemplate. For this reason, you might consider a rather long conversational "on ramp".

Strategy: Point out that whites are not alone in feeling racial threat.

1. Bring up examples of non-white groups feeling racial threat.
2. Discuss what the skeptic thinks about these situations and whether these feelings are understandable.
3. Explain the concept of racial threat.
4. Demonstrate that you have empathy for feelings of racial threat by sharing an experience in which you felt it.
5. Explore together whether the skeptic or you have ever seen situations where a white person was clearly feeling racial threat. (Examples of people close to you who are not avowed racists are likely to be best).
6. Probe the skeptic for times when they might have had feelings that could reasonably be called racial threat. (See the reflection questions as potential prompts.)

7. In many cases, it will be useful to let some time go by before the next steps.
8. Have an exploratory conversation about how racial threat might manifest in ways that are not obvious to whites at first. This might include examples when people of color have brought up the idea of racial threat (probably not using that term) and whites did not perceive it.
9. You may also want to explore how this dynamic has often remained invisible to most whites.

REFLECTION QUESTIONS

1. Think of 2-3 times when you had an internal reaction that may have emerged from racial threat. Examples might include:
   - » Feeling like your neighborhood is being "invaded" by others
   - » Wondering what will happen to people "like you" if an organization continues to change with new populations
2. Become familiar with at least two dynamics where non-white groups have experienced racial threat. Given the level of gentrification that negatively impacts historically-black cities such as Brooklyn, Harlem, Detroit, and Austin, this is not difficult. After doing a few minutes of internet research to familiarize yourself with 2-3 examples, jot down your talking points.

Recall 2-3 times when a white person who was not an avowed racist demonstrated a perspective that demonstrated racial threat.

RACIAL BACKLASH AND RACIAL DENIAL

WHAT IT IS

Racial backlash describes the collective negative reaction of a large number of white people to a perceived advance by POC. It is an attempt to restore the racial order. Racial denial is often paired with backlash and describes the ways that white people often refuse to acknowledge racist motivations. It is part of what happens when people are engaging in backlash behaviors.

Even though backlash and denial are largely collective behaviors, they can sometimes be observed, with discernment, at the level of the individual. Still, it is more difficult to get skeptics to acknowledge this phenomenon than the previous concepts in this primer.

WHY IT IS IMPORTANT

Over the course of American history, there are numerous times when white communities have exhibited a negative response to changes in the racial order. When this happens, many whites do not feel they are involved in a backlash against POC, but rather think of themselves as merely doing what is good for themselves and for society as a whole.

HOW IT MANIFESTS

American history is replete with moments of white racial backlash. There are too many to list individually. Your task is to brush up on a few diverse examples so that you can answer 2-3 follow-up questions when a skeptic challenges you. To review a few examples:

- Laws that limited individual freedoms – such as the Black Codes passed after the Civil War
- Riots that aim to destroy entire communities – see Tulsa OK and Rosewood FL in the 1920s, Detroit and St. Louis in the 1940s
- Community mobilizations to oppose integration, such when blacks tried to integrate Levittown, PA
- Uncoordinated large-scale migration – such as white flight in hundreds of major cities

- Coordinated acts of withdrawal from collective structures such as public schools. One example is the closing of public schools to avoid integration in Prince Edward County, VA.
- Passing laws that have the effect of restricting minority political power, such as poll taxes and literacy tests in the 20th century. (Although it seems clear that 21st century Voter ID laws fit this pattern, you probably should not bring this up since this is a live public issue with active propaganda in today's news. Instead, let the skeptic come to reconsider such laws after they become comfortable with the topic being relevant in previous eras.)

WHY AND HOW SKEPTICS RESIST

- Racial backlash implies a widespread enforcement of a racial order by large numbers of white people.
- Without a sophisticated attitude about what racism is and how it is supported by otherwise "good people", the skeptic's sense of comfort that they are innocent may be challenged by the solidarity implied by racial backlash, because they do not harbor consciously racist views.
- If you have not laid the groundwork to get the skeptic's buy-in to the idea that individuals can manifest racially motivated behaviors unconsciously, racial backlash will likely be extremely difficult for them to accept. In fact, the skeptic may be challenged enough by racial backlash that they may retract their prior admissions to some of the individually focused concepts covered previously in this workbook.

SOME CONVERSATIONAL STRATEGIES

There are two core challenges: 1) to overcome their denial that these backlashes are part of a pattern of behavior by white populations and 2) to get the skeptic to see that good people can participate in racial backlashes at varying levels of conscious racism, including very low levels.

A potentially fruitful way of overcoming these barriers is to search your own personal and family history for examples of participating in a collective behavior that could reasonably be regarded as part of a racial backlash. Because you are talking about people that you presumably regard with some esteem, you might get the skeptic past the idea that only "bad people" are part of backlashes and denial. Moreover, it will be helpful if you can recount how those participating looked at their decisions at the time.

REFLECTION QUESTIONS

1. Search your memory for 1-2 times when you or people you respect participated in or supported a group response that could be reasonably thought of as racial backlash/denial. Try to capture how they thought about the situation at the time.
2. If there is one, jot a few notes down about a time when someone claimed something was white racial backlash/denial, and you rejected this way of thinking. If you now think this was a backlash, be prepared to discuss how your view evolved. If you still think this was not, be prepared to discuss why you question the backlash label in this case, although you do not question that backlashes exist. (This question is encouraging you to find a "But later, I realized" story.)
3. If you have had strong emotions about the above situations, try to recall what they were and why you felt them.
4. What do you think is the obligation of good white people who realize that they have been a part of a racial backlash previously but did not see this at the time? What level of obligation do you think is appropriate, and why do you feel this way?

Suggested Strategy:

1. Discuss a situation in which a white person you love or respect took actions that were aligned with racial backlash/denial. It is important to step inside their narrative – remember, they did not likely think that their motivations were based on irrational racism.
2. Reinforce that you do not see the person as having bad character, but rather as an unwitting participant in a system that tends to keep white people from seeing the full implications of personal decisions that reinforce the racial status quo.
3. If you have one, relate a time when someone made the case about

backlash/denial and you rejected this way of thinking. Relate your rationale for why you did not see the situation in this way. Discuss how you subsequently came to different conclusions once you became more aware of how racial backlashes/denial work.

4. If you had some emotions about these conclusions, discuss them as obstacles to seeing things clearly, if appropriate.
5. Having explained the concept broadly and provided multiple examples of how racial backlash/denial works, see if the skeptic can think of examples from their personal or family history.
6. Reinforce empathy for the central characters who participated unknowingly.
7. Have a discussion about the appropriate way to evaluate people's decisions about white backlashes/denial once they have an understanding of how they work.
8. If you have brought them along this far, declare victory! Do NOT try to get them to admit anything. Let them simmer on the conversation.

OVERVIEW OF SOME IMPORTANT IDEAS ABOUT CUMULATIVE RACISM

The concepts that we have reviewed in the previous section (othering, unconscious bias, attribution error, racial anxiety, unearned racial advantage, racial threat and racial denial/backlash) should be the core set of concepts that you focus on with skeptics. All can be understood by a combination of thorough self-reflection and perhaps some conversations with others that are approached in an open minded way. Put differently, each of these concepts can be directly experienced by individuals, even if doing so requires a very detailed and courageous examination of one's experience.

By contrast, the concepts in this section (systemic racism, structural racism, and racial inequity) are to a much greater extent, cumulative or group level concepts. In order to understand them, it is necessary to go outside of the experiences of oneself or a handful of people. They can only be understood by integrating statistics, historical information, or other sources of input beyond personal experiences.

These concepts may be easier for skeptics to grapple with and potentially accept in a group context such as a workshop. In fact, some allies tell us that they have found that in workshops of conservatives and liberals, focusing on non-personal issues of racism is more productive.[10] But in one-on-one and very small group work trying to break through racism denial, you may not want to focus on large concepts such as those about to be discussed. Because these large concepts require external sources of information, you are subject to getting push-back about the sources of the data you are referencing, the ideological bias of the information, and similar matters.

---

10 "I went to a symposium with conservatives and liberals and one thing that worked was to not stress the interpersonal part. Which is where people who deny racism tend to get turned out. But again, stress it from a more structural piece. This was more effective." - Participant in White Ally Toolkit Workshop, Pasadena CA

Talking about these aspects of cumulative racism are important in racial awareness-raising. But these conversations are more likely to be productive if you already have piqued the curiosity of the skeptic about the possibility that racism is a much bigger problem than they had previously considered. In order for these conversations to be productive, your skeptic must be open to the possibility that people can enact behaviors with racially disparate results without knowing it.

If your personal anecdotes have not influenced your skeptic to accept that individuals can be inadvertently racist, it may be difficult for statistics, analogies, and logical reasoning to persuade them that individual-level racism can accumulate to produce broader effects. Although it seems clear, this supposition needs to be tested. For this reason, the following pages offer possibilities for how you might move a skeptic forward on these issues.

In the upcoming review of these issues, it is not presumed that the skeptic is wholeheartedly embracing a racially progressive worldview; they are still a skeptic. But the presumption is that you (or some set of circumstances) have brought them along to a basic openness to individual-level concepts of racism.

INSTITUTIONAL RACISM

WHAT IT IS

Institutional racism is the result of historic, conscious, and unconscious racism combining to produce an institution treating large numbers of POC worse than white people.

WHY IT IS IMPORTANT

Personal bigotry by whites against POC has declined in the last fifty years. It is easy for skeptics to think that racism does not exist if their only notion of racism is one based in individual attitudes and explicit laws. Some experts have argued that we are in a time of "racism without racists"[11] and getting people to see this is a critical step in advancing racial equity.

Talking about these aspects of cumulative racism is important in racial awareness-raising. But these conversations are more likely to be productive if you already have piqued the curiosity of the skeptic about the possibility that racism is a much bigger problem than they had previously considered.

STRATEGIES FOR RAISING THE ISSUE

Institutional racism is a widely discussed topic, so it will not be reviewed here. The relevant question is how to guide a skeptic toward and through a conversation about it, with the best chance of not activating their resistance.

11 Racism Without Racists: Color-blind Racism and the Persistence of Racial Inequality in the United States, Edward Bonilla-Silva, 2010, Rowman & Littlefield.

It is may be useful to point out a few examples of the way that organizations have disparate impacts on different groups. It is probably best to do some background research on organizations that do not seem far afield from you and the skeptic's direct experience. One strategy is to do some light research about organizations that you are now or have ever been connected to. For instance, you might look at what is known about disparate outcomes related to law enforcement in places you have lived, or the disparate rates of progress of different racial groups up the promotion ladder at places you have worked. The heart of this strategy is to raise the possibility of institutional racism being an aspect of organizations that one of you is connected to and perhaps even have affection for.

An alternative approach is to get information about community institutions in the location where the skeptic lives now, or where you live or have lived. The objective would be to help the skeptic see that these racially-disparate impacts can occur right around us, and this can happen in a way that many good white folks don't see.

WHAT RESISTANCE MIGHT LOOK LIKE

Many skeptics have a deep emotional connection to the idea that society's institutions are racially fair. One way they will resist evidence to the contrary is to question your sources of information. Thus, it is important to justify your ideas about institutional unfairness against claims that your sources of information are wrong. As you are getting information to validate your point, take note of how likely your source will be considered ideologically biased.

REFLECTION QUESTIONS

1. Which of the individual equity obstacles can you most compellingly tell a personal anecdote about? If you have discussed more than one with skeptics, which have served as the focus of the best conversation?
2. Which of the personal equity obstacles can you best connect to institutional racism? (Note: Generally, unconscious bias and racial anxiety are easiest for many people.)
3. What institutions have you been associated with where there is mostly undisputed evidence of their racism?

4. What are some institutions that are connected to the skeptic (or better, both of you) that have undisputed links to racism?
5. What is the narrative describing how you have arrived at your current understanding of institutional racism? In other words, what will you say to persuade the skeptic that you once thought like they did?

SOME CONVERSATIONAL STRATEGIES

Strategy 1: Begin with your participation in one of the individual impediments, then move the conversation to institutions.

1. Re-examine which of the preceding six individual equity impediments discussed previously (othering, unconscious bias, attribution error, racial anxiety, racial threat, racial backlash) would be the easiest to get the skeptic to consider that they participated in.
2. Think through/learn about how this impediment can accumulate over time and many people to cause institutional effects.
3. At an opportunity that feels reasonably natural, bring up the topic of institutional racism. It's best if you can link it to a personal experience, even if it's just someone else's story that was told to you.
4. After probing a bit about their perspective on institutional racism, try to connect with it. If you have ever thought that a claim of institutional racism was inaccurate, bring this up if this would be helpful in connecting with your skeptic. It may be important to demonstrate that you don't think such claims are inherently accurate.
5. Discuss a thought experiment related to whichever impediment is the most fertile to discuss. Brainstorm what might happen if many white people in an institution were affected by unconscious bias, racial anxiety, or another interpersonal aspects of racism when interacting with people of color. Explore the possibility that if many white folks' actions were influenced by this impediment, the cumulative result might very well be labeled as institutional racism.
6. If you have discovered it, bring up corroborating evidence that institutional racism may take this form. Your personal experiences are most powerful, but second-hand ones can be helpful, too. If you have facts and data, only bring them to the conversation if your skeptic is

the kind of person who is persuadable by data.[12]

7. Be careful to frequently gauge how you are doing as the conversation progresses. Remember, your objective is not to deliver a lecture or turn them off.

Strategy 2: Go directly to a discussion about institutional behavior.

If your skeptic has embraced the idea that the two of you are on a multi-conversation inquiry about racism, you may be able to skip steps 1-4 above.

12 Some scientists have found that about 25% of both conservatives and liberals have a trait called "scientific curiosity'; this trait is demonstrated by these people's willingness to be influenced by facts that tend to contradict their natural political leanings. From: http://www.pbs.org/wgbh/nova/next/body/scientific-curiosity-could-bridge-partisan-divide-new-study-says/

STRUCTURAL RACISM

WHAT IT IS

Structural racism signifies the way that institutional racism across multiple sectors of life can have an even further compounding effect on POC. This compounding effect severely undermines any efforts by individuals, institutions, or sectors to move towards the elimination of racial disparities.

WHY IT IS IMPORTANT

Lurking in the backdrop of many racism skeptics (and others) is the idea that the reason that POC have poor life outcomes across almost all measures (increased mortality, poor health, less wealth, higher unemployment, less educational attainment, higher incarceration, etc.) is because they are inherently inferior. Structural racism provides an alternative explanation by highlighting the way that POC's ability to improve their life situation is impeded by racism across multiple dimensions of their lives. This concept helps explain why communities of color have experienced only modest improvement in reversing centuries of disadvantage in the last few decades of relative progress.

HOW IT MANIFESTS

Example #1:

Racial profiling in policing causes a POC to be fined for not wearing a seatbelt as a teenager. Poverty (and procrastination) contributes to the teenager not addressing the citation and accumulating unpayable additional fees as a result. These unpaid fees make in impossible to get a driver's license. Because of the history of residential segregation and racially-influenced regional decisions to not connect heavily black areas to regional employment hubs (racial backlash), the young person has less access to suitable jobs and struggles with chronic unemployment.

Example #2:

Historic and current factors in residential segregation are producing food deserts in many communities of color around the country. The lack of access to affordable nutritious food leads many people in such communities to have diets that cause diabetes. The lack of local parks and other civic infrastructure (such as well-maintained sidewalks or bike lanes) inhibit walking and other inexpensive exercise options. In addition, previous racism-influenced decisions about the location of medical facilities resulted in fewer and lower quality clinics and hospitals in these same neighborhoods. This in turn results in more severe diagnoses when people are finally discovered to have such diet-related ailments.

Note: One of the most important ideas behind structural racism is that the forces that perpetuate racial disparities do not depend on "racist" people to enact them. Rather, a number of forces work wickedly and synergistically to inhibit progress on racial disparities. It will likely be very difficult to get a skeptic to contemplate the idea of structural racism if they don't already believe that institutional racism exists.

WHY AND HOW SKEPTICS RESIST

Structural racism takes the analysis of race to a very high level of abstraction and may be resisted by people who don't naturally think this way. Further, the concept strikes deeply at the idea that society is basically working well.

Some skeptics may want to retract their support of individual-level concepts when they see possible connections to systemic societal flaws. This is why it is important to make sure the conversational foundation you have laid is strong. Before you raise the issue of structural racism, it is advisable to confirm that they have bought into the ideas that there are multiple ways that interpersonal racism shows up, and that there are multiple sectors where institutional racism impedes POC's progress.

Remember, this issue will stretch the discomfort of skeptics – especially conservative ones – so be careful not to raise it until you have indications that they are ready.

RACIAL INEQUITY AND RACIAL EQUITY

WHAT IT IS

- Racial inequity is the way that racial status is a strong statistical predictor of worse outcomes for people in different groups, regardless of their individual circumstances.
- Racial equity is an idealized non-existent state in which one's racial status is not predictive of outcomes.

WHY IT IS IMPORTANT

One of the tricky ironies of modern racism is that the word "racism" and especially "racist" have become triggers that make it difficult for skeptics to keep listening to substantive analytical points about how society works. It is useful to have a term for the racially-problematic cumulative outcome that does not depend on the word "racism" or "racist. For example, "racially disparate outcomes" or "racial inequity" are often not as triggering.

Even with this embedded resistance to plain language, for many people, the most compelling way to discuss the large scale racial disparities is to refer to the fact that race of a newborn has a significant predictive factor about life expectancy, wealth level, chance of incarceration, level of education, and many other factors. Some allies use the frame of "racial equity" to describe a future state where race is not predictive of babies' quality and quantity of life.

It is worth noting that there are some other factors that affect how you can maximize the usefulness of this term.

Many skeptics – especially ideological conservatives - resist societal interventions that appear to not accommodate the fact that people have different levels of talent and exert different levels of effort. Compared to the word "equality", using the word "equity" may make it less likely that a skeptic will gird up for an argument over talents and capacities. To many, racial equality implies guaranteeing equal outcomes. By contrast, you can frame "racial equity" as implying a guarantee of equal opportunities to groups, but in a way that recognizes existing impediments to opportunities.

It remains true that people who are skeptical that racism is real often harbor a perspective that paying more attention to racial disparities will lead to society making unfettered giveaways to undeserving people. In this way, the idea that some groups need more assistance may be very challenging. If you frame equity as about equalizing opportunity instead of outcomes, you will be less likely to raise their concern about the welfare state running amok.

You will need to experiment with when and how to approach the issue of racial equity and notice how it affects your work with skeptics.

PART FOUR: ODDS AND ENDS

Part Four includes instruments and commentary that did not fit well within other sections but will likely be useful to many allies who are increasing their focus on influencing skeptics.

PART FOUR

ODDS AND ENDS

This closing section is comprised of a number of short essays and brief instruments that are relevant to the tasks of becoming a more effective anti-racism ally. These pieces include:

PAST EXPERIENCES OF PEOPLE TRYING TO INFLUENCE EACH OTHER

At some point, other anti-racism advocates will question the efficacy of empathetic listening-based approaches. In fact, you may begin to question them yourself. This reflection instrument encourages you – perhaps with another person – to review a number of past experiences where you were trying to influence others or someone was trying to influence you to think differently. The instrument encourages you to think back on the style of engagement that was used and the impact it had so that you can assess which approaches appear to have the better track record.

CONTINUUM OF RETORTS

There will be moments when someone displays or articulates a racially-problematic attitude that needs to be challenged but the setting is poorly suited for real engagement. There are many options for how to respond in this situation, and these options vary widely with respect to intensity and how much you are challenging the person. Even within the constraint of non-violent communication, responses can vary greatly. This short document gives several examples to illustrate a continuum of responses.

SHAME: DOES IT AFFECT YOUR WORK AS AN ALLY?

During workshops around the country, several allies have argued that the shame they feel about their own progress on race can undermine how effectively they engage both racism skeptics and even other allies. This short instrument asks a few reflection questions to encourage you to consider how much and what type of shame might be affecting your anti-racism practice.

CHOOSING SKEPTICS TO ENGAGE

Allies need to learn how to make good choices about which skeptics they invest time and energy in trying to change. This short instrument encourages you to consider a few factors to make better choices about which skeptics to spend your energy on.

CREATING AN INFORMAL ALLY PRACTICE GROUP

This essay reviews reasons why it might be worth your time to recruit a few white ally friends to join you to intentionally improve your practice of engaging skeptics. Embedded within the essay is a short instrument encouraging you to think about different characteristics of your anti-racist friends to discern who might be most suitable to be part of a small practice group. The essay also advocates that ally organizations make supporting such groups a part of their major initiatives.

CREATING A FORMAL PRACTICE GROUP WITH A FACILITATOR

This workbook focuses on the specific setting of a white ally talking with white racism skeptics in a one-on-one or very small group setting. Some readers may be tempted to use these approaches as the basis of conversations among groups of people, all white or perhaps racially mixed.

If you are going to adapt the materials in this way, it is recommended that you engage a facilitator with some degree of experience.

USING INSIGHTS ABOUT CONSERVATIVE AND LIBERAL MORAL FRAMEWORKS

In the past two decades, researchers have made significant advances in understanding important cross-cultural patterns in how human societies create moral frameworks. It turns out that there are some general differences between ideological conservatives and ideological liberals regarding which underlying values are most important. As noted in the introduction to the workbook, the conversation between allies and skeptics largely (though not at all universally) reflects this liberal/ conservative split. This brief essay reviews some conservative v. liberal differences in moral frameworks and orientations, and suggests a few tweaks to the storytelling suggested by the RACE Method that leverage these frameworks. Attached to the essay is a short instrument that encourages you to look at differences in orientation between you and two skeptics you might consider for the focus of your persuasive efforts.

WHY ANTI-RACIST PROGRESSIVES NEED TO SUPPORT CONSERVATIVES

This short essay presents the reasons why it is important that progressive anti-racists maintain a belief in the possibility of an anti-racist conservatism, even if they have never seen anyone fitting this description.

CLOSING ENCOURAGEMENTS

An essay on the importance of maintaining a focus on influencing skeptics, in the face of various factors that may distract you.

PAST EXPERIENCES OF PEOPLE TRYING TO INFLUENCE EACH OTHER

This workbook is written from the perspective that approaches to influencing racism skeptics based on empathetic listening are more effective in changing people's perspective than those based on debate, verbal combat, and confrontation. This is not the most common view within the anti-racism community, and there may be times when it is useful for you and/or others to review approaches to influencing people. The following questions are designed to foster a review of your actual experiences with different approaches to engaging other people. For best results, answer the questions as they are stated; if the question is not framed specifically around race conversations, consider a broad range of conversations you have had on many topics besides race.

Have you ever observed situations where someone's views were hardened after they received a private lecture from someone who thought they knew "the truth"? If so, jot a few notes about these experiences below.

Have you ever observed situations where someone's views were authentically changed for the better after they received a private lecture from someone who thought they knew "the truth?" If so, jot a few notes about these experiences below.

If there have ever been times when someone listened to you empathetically (not necessarily about race), as part of a conversation that helped expand your view of a situation, jot a few notes about these experiences here.

If there have been times when you listened to someone closely and empathetically (not necessarily about race) and this helped someone else expand their view of a situation, jot a few notes about these experiences here.

For most people, their own experience suggests that listening-based strategies work better. (If this is not the case, you might consider creating a workbook for white allies that replicates the success of private lectures built on combative rhetoric). Non-combatively engaging people who have made racially-problematic statements requires a difficult act of self-discipline – so a good deal of motivation is necessary. Hopefully, remembering your past experiences with confrontational versus empathetic listening approaches can help you muster that discipline when needed.

CONTINUUM OF RETORTS

There are times when people say racially-problematic things that, if unchallenged, tend to make a social atmosphere feel noxious. In addition, letting such statements go by unchallenged makes most allies feel as though they are not fulfilling an important duty. In these situations, many allies feel that their only options are at one extreme 1) doing nothing, or at the other extreme 2) aggressively calling out people for being racist.

In fact, even if you want to stay within the realm of non-violent communication (and you may not want to constrain yourself in this way) there are still many options you can muster in the face of these racially-problematic statements. The following potential responses are purposely arranged from the ones that are the least confrontative to the ones that are much more confrontative.

- **Feigned Deafness** – "Excuse me, I did not hear you. Do you want to say that again?"
- **Feigned Ignorance** – "I don't understand what you mean." (This is especially good for racist jokes, since explaining any type of joke tends to drain the humor from it.)
- **Feigned Doubt of Sincerity** – "You don't mean that, do you?"
- **Challenge Veracity** – "Surely, you don't think_____. Don't we know that is not true?"
- **Raise Impact on Hypothetical Others** – "I wonder how ______would feel if they heard you say that? "
- **Raise Perception Issues for Them** – "You might consider if you want to say something like that in this setting." (This is especially useful at work.)
- **Express Your Boundaries** – "I do not want to be a part of conversations where these things are said."
- **Link to Your Feelings about Them** – "This is so awful.... I don't want to be around you right now."

- **Implicate their Character** – "This is the kind of statement I have only heard bigots say."
- **Warning** – "If I ever hear you say something like that again, I will tell ________" (e.g. Human Resources if the setting is the workplace).
- **Public Reporting** – "______will hear about this conversation" (e.g. Human Resources).

SHAME: DOES IT AFFECT YOUR WORK AS AN ALLY?

There are a few types of shame that white allies have talked about in workshops for this project. Anti-racist allies can feel shame about:

- How long it took them to realize how extensive and important are the problems of racial inequities, bias, and privilege.
- The fact that they are still subject to having biased thoughts.
- The relatively low amount of emotionally-close contacts they have across racial lines.

For many people, feelings of shame can begin to emerge as they consider engaging a skeptic. It sometimes leads allies to avoid having conversations with skeptics, and sometimes leads them to more combative (and even shaming) approaches. In order to approach the conversation from a centered place, it is important to reflect on the degree to which shame might be part of your emotional factors. The following questions are designed to help you reflect on the way that shame might be affecting you and your interactions.

I feel some degree of shame about the fact that that it took as long as it did for me to become somewhat "woke" about racial issues.

- Strongly agree
- Agree
- Somewhat agree/somewhat disagree
- Disagree
- Strongly disagree

I feel some degree of shame about the fact that I still sometimes have racist/prejudiced/biased thoughts.

- Strongly agree
- Agree
- Somewhat agree/somewhat disagree
- Disagree
- Strongly disagree

I feel some degree of shame about the low amount of substantive contact I have with people of color.

- Strongly agree
- Agree
- Somewhat agree/somewhat disagree
- Disagree
- Strongly disagree

If you were to be totally honest with yourself, how much do you think that shame may affect your effectiveness with skeptics?

- No impact
- Very little impact
- A little impact
- Some impact
- A lot of impact
- A dominant factor

If you were to be totally honest with yourself, how much do you think that shame may affect your effectiveness with other people who you think of as, broadly speaking, anti-racism allies?

- No impact
- Very little impact
- A little impact
- Some impact
- A lot of impact
- A dominant factor

The best way to overcome shame around this issue is to talk about it with other white allies who might also have similar feelings. People can usually muster more empathy and grace for others than they can for themselves. Further, being in a group with other allies who are trying to control the impact that shame is having on their conversations will likely lead you to provide reassurance and support to them. For the sake of your own progress and healing, it is useful to hear yourself giving this type of grace to others.

CHOOSING SKEPTICS TO ENGAGE

The intention of the White Ally Toolkit is that you will not only be able to respond well to racially-problematic statements that occur unexpectedly, but that you will also make a conscious choice to engage some people in your circle of influence. No matter how much time and energy you decide to invest in influencing skeptics, you will still need to make decisions about which people you invest in. This raises the question: If you are choosing between a number of racism skeptics, what are the qualities most associated with your potential to have an effect on them?

One factor to consider is how much the skeptic has a tendency to push you out of empathetic listening mode. The methods discussed here work better if you are in a centered emotional place, and people vary in how much they trigger you. You should look at your interpersonal practice of influencing skeptics to acknowledge racism as a lifelong practice and one that you are likely to improve over time. As a result, it may be most fruitful to initially focus on those who trigger your emotions less, so that you can have a more detached attitude toward the conversations.

As you assess possible candidates for your efforts, consider their general level of open-mindedness. One model of open-mindedness is that this is an amalgam of a number of different qualities, namely:

- Thirst for learning
- Curiosity
- An ability to see things from different perspectives
- An acceptance and respect for other people's beliefs and choices
- Awareness that one's own beliefs and filters can be limiting

A third factor to consider is the level of empathy, which some define as the ability to feel what other people are feeling. One of the reasons that many allies care about racial equity is because they have cultivated empathy for POC and the situations they confront. Think about whether each skeptic generally empathizes with other people, even if you don't have direct knowledge of them doing this with POC.

As has been said, you should consider a variety of factors in making a decision about turning a moment of conversation into an on-ramp for a dialogue about race. The following worksheet is designed to help your decision-making.

List the top 6 people that you are most inclined to focus energy on to influence them to see racism differently.

1. ______________________________

2. ______________________________

3. ______________________________

4. ______________________________

5. ______________________________

6. ______________________________

You will now order them from most to least on the three qualities discussed above: how much they trigger you; how open-minded they are, and how empathetic they tend to be.

	Least likely to trigger you	Most open-minded	Most empathetic
1			
2			
3			
4			
5			
6			
	Most likely to trigger you	Least open -minded	Least empathetic

You should consider other factors, such as how frequently you interact with them, how comfortable your interactions are, the degree to which you have common interests that can reinforce your sense of connectedness, etc. The hope is that the exercise above contributes to your reflection on the many factors that matter to making good choices. If you have never made an intentional medium- to long-term effort to influence a skeptic, you should consider first focusing on people who tend to fall toward the top of these scales. Reflecting on the above, place the skeptics in order that reflects the most likelihood of achieving success as you attempt to influence them.

Most Likely

1. ______________________________
2. ______________________________
3. ______________________________
4. ______________________________
5. ______________________________
6. ______________________________

Least Likely

You should consider how many people you want to engage on racial issues, regardless of whether they make racially-problematic statements. It would be great if every white ally chose more people every year, as long as this effort is sustainable. The hope is that allies will make engaging people in this way a lifelong practice. This might mean starting slowly with a smaller number of skeptics, learning about your own strengths and weaknesses in doing this work, and expanding your practice over a period of time.

CREATING AN INFORMAL ALLY PRACTICE GROUP

This workbook is intended to be of use to any ally to increase their influence with racism skeptics in their circle. The hope is that the reflection exercises and encouragement to practice will be valuable even if the reader is completely isolated from other allies. That said, you will improve influence with racism skeptics much faster if you are in a learning community with other allies who are trying to master the methods here.

There are myriad subtleties that distinguish allies who are very effective and those who are only moderately effective in influencing racism skeptics. Accordingly, there are many questions to think about when using the methods here as a practice. Do certain approaches work better than others with certain types of skeptics? When is the best time to shift from talking about experiences to talking about data? Are there common sentiments that skeptics express that are not well addressed here?

To become both totally comfortable and masterful at the conversational approaches in this workbook, you will need to go through the common quality improvement cycle of test, observe, reflect, improve. If you are in a group with others who are trying to improve their engagement practice, you will learn much more by listening to other people's reflections. Perhaps more importantly, you will probably do more reflection if you know you have regular opportunities to share your experiences with others.

If there is not a ready-made group, you should consider forming your own group. You are not the only white person who is troubled by the way that racism denial among whites is limiting progress on racial equity. It might not be difficult to gather a few friends who get something out of experimenting with different responses to racism skeptics and reflecting on their effectiveness. Such moments need not be formal, large, validated by an official organization, or free of adult beverages. In addition, these moments of collective reflection might happen online or through conference calls.

It is useful to think about people in your circle – defined broadly – who you might want to see regularly (say, bi-weekly or monthly) to talk about your influence practice. First, think of the six folks that you are most drawn to considering for a three-person racial ally support group. Write their names here.

1. ______________________________

2. ______________________________

3. ______________________________

4. ______________________________

5. ______________________________

6. ______________________________

In addition to typical factors you use to choose people, the following characteristics seem of particular importance.

- Willingness to try to push oneself past limitations
- Capacity to be reflective
- Graciousness to others (and themselves) when goals are not met
- Level of commitment to racial equity

Next you are going to analyze your list of potential practice supporters. Below is a table with the four characteristics above and a blank space for criteria you think is particularly important, too. As you rate the ally, compare them to other people who are allies in the broad definition of that word. (That is, it is OK if they have never gone to a white ally meeting.)

	Pushes self 4=really strong 1=relatively weak	Capacity to reflect	Gracious-ness	Commitment to racial equity
1.				
2.				
3.				
4.				
5.				
6.				

Ideally, you should not have to form a group on your own. Organizations that are committed to anti-racism may, at least nominally, support ally practice groups. Admittedly, this may not be likely, since as of 2018, few groups recognize the importance of this specific approach to anti-racism work. Nevertheless, if you are interested in refining your skills, you should consider whether such organizations might support a practice group, even with only the validation of verbal support.

If you are a member of an organization that supports white allies, you should propose such learning groups be considered as an important initiative. Increasing influence on racism skeptics is not the only activity that ally groups should do, of course. But it is less common than other activities like protesting or pushing for institutional change. In order to create racial equity in the long run, ally groups need to be active on many issues that all support the same outcome.

CREATING A FORMAL PRACTICE GROUP WITH A FACILITATOR

This workbook focuses on the specific setting of a white ally talking with white racism skeptics in a one-on-one or very small group setting. Some readers may be tempted to use these approaches as the basis of conversations among groups of people, all white or perhaps racially mixed.

If you are going to adapt the materials in this way, it is recommended that you engage a facilitator with some degree of experience. Facilitating productive group conversation has its own set of skills that are needed to ensure a conversation on such a sensitive topic goes well. It is useful if this facilitator has experience with racial conversations in particular.

A facilitator who is contemplating adapting the conversational approach in this workbook should be able to do so with relative ease, since it is based on an underlying theory of dialogue. The core of that theory posits that dialogue happens best if people: 1) share personal experiences about an issue, then 2) try to make sense of the larger social dynamics behind an issue, by collectively examining the similarities and differences in experience. This theory of dialogue is explained in The Little Book of Dialogue for Difficult Subjects, by Lisa Schirch and David Campt.

To assist with engaging groups, the White Ally Toolkit is developing a Facilitator's Supplement. It will guide people to lead ally groups through this workbook, over 5-10 sessions.

USING INSIGHTS ABOUT CONSERVATIVE AND LIBERAL MORAL FRAMEWORKS

Among scholars who study moral development, a leading theory is called "moral foundations", which posits that the vast majority of moral frameworks in human societies fall along five essential dimensions.[1]

1. **Care:** cherishing and protecting others; opposite of **harm.**
2. **Fairness or Proportionality:** rendering justice according to shared rules; opposite of **cheating.**
3. **Loyalty or Ingroup:** standing with your group, family, nation; opposite of **betrayal.**
4. **Authority or Respect:** submitting to tradition and legitimate authority; opposite of **subversion.**
5. **Sanctity or Purity:** abhorrence for disgusting things, foods, actions; opposite of **degradation.**

According to this theory, most cultures and subcultures base what is deemed proper or improper behavior as existing along some combination of these differing values. Significantly, however, different cultures value each of these dimensions to varying degrees. Jonathan Haidt, author of the bestselling The Righteous Mind, argues that American liberals emphasize the values of caring and fairness and have a very low valuation of loyalty, authority, and sanctity. By contrast, American conservatives tend to value all five dimensions to about the same extent.

The following table summarizes some of these differences and the way that people with different ideologies tend to define these dimensions.

1 https://en.wikipedia.org/wiki/Moral_foundations_theory

Common (not universal) differences in Moral Frameworks

Construct	Conservative Moral Framework	Liberal Moral Framework
Harm/Caring (Liberals tend to care a lot about this)	Family = Ingroup	Family = Humanity/ Outgroups
Justice/Fairness (Liberals tend to care a lot about this)	Achieved, inherited, karma, divinely destined	Egalitarian/social justice/ meritocratic
Ingroup/Loyalty (Conservatives tend to care a lot about this)	Ingroup/nation	Class/humanity
Authority (Conservatives tend to care a lot about this)	Traditions, hierarchical authority, religious beliefs	Science, rational philosophy, empiricism
Purity/Sanctity (Conservatives tend to care a lot about this)	Traditional values, patriotism, fetuses	Environment, planet, women's body/choice

As important as these differences in moral frameworks are, Haidt and other scholars posit moral ideology is only one aspect of the difference between the conservative and liberal perspective. Their argument is that that conservative and liberal political perspectives correlate with specific orientations to life. Broadly speaking, a conservative orientation to life values order, routine, similarity, and familiarity. In contrast, a liberal orientation prioritizes novelty, uniqueness, and diversity. According to Haidt, people who identify as conservative tend to like order and predictability. They are not attracted to change for the sake of change, whereas people who identify as liberal like variety and diversity. One study uses dots moving around on a screen; it was found that conservatives like the images where the dots are moving around more in lockstep with each other.

Liberals prefer when it's all chaotic and random. Liberals keep their rooms messier than conservatives. So these are deep, psychological differences. We eat different foods, at different restaurants. And this is part of the problem now--not just an ideological difference but a real lifestyle difference.

Common (not universal) Differences in Personality Orientations

Common Tendencies Among Liberals	Common Tendencies Among Conservatives
Value novelty in experiences (travel, diet, personal identification)	Prefer the safety and predictability of routine and sameness
See institutions as instruments of caring for people	Value the stability of institutions in themselves
Believe in change and risk	Believe in order and safety
Often seek justice, even at risk to themselves	Often seek order, even at the expense of the most vulnerable
Tend to question authority	Tend to revere authority
Speak for the vulnerable	Speak for institutions
Celebrate diversity and flux among groups not in-group membership	Celebrate loyalty to groups, and stability among them

Taking moral and lifestyle orientations into account may help refine your engagement of racism skeptics. This will be discussed below. But first, let's take a quick inventory of these differences the scholars talk about.

The following instrument may help you reflect on differences in orientation you have with racism skeptics that you are working on.

ASSESSING POLITICS AND LIFESTYLES

Step 1: Put your first initial on where you are on the scales. Be honest

			MIDLINE			
Very Liberal						Very Conservative
Very Messy						Very Neat
Values change/ risk						Values order/ safety
Questions Authority						Values Authority
Values Novelty/variety						Prefers predictability, sameness

Draw a solid line that connects all of your initials, so you can easily see the pattern.

Step 2: I have a bias against folks who are politically conservative. (Circle one).

Strongly Disagree	Disagree	Slightly Disagree	Slightly Agree	Agree	Strongly Agree

Step 3: Do Step 1 again, this time assessing a racism skeptic (let's call them Skeptic #1) in your circle and using their initials. When you are done, use a dotted to connect the initials of Skeptic #1. Notice how much or how little your lines are close or cross each other.

Step 4: Do Step 1 again, this time using the initials of another skeptic (Skeptic #2). Draw a double line to connect their initials. Notice again how much or little your lines are close or cross each other.

Reflection: How do the patterns of answers to the questions above relate to your challenge in engaging racism skeptics, if at all?

REFINING YOUR ENGAGEMENT PRACTICE IN LIGHT OF CONSERVATIVE V. LIBERAL PERSPECTIVES

These differences in both moral foundations and basic orientation have significant implications for American political and interpersonal discourse, and for conversations between conservatives and liberals. Some moral foundation scholars suggest that one problem with political discourse, is that people base arguments about correct behavior on their own moral foundations rather than that of the person with whom they are speaking. These scholars suggest it is more effective to make arguments for their position using the moral frameworks of their counterpart.

The differences around basic orientation can affect discussions about politics and many other things. Think of one about proper immigration levels and policies. An uninitiated liberal person might be inclined to discuss the way that immigration has contributed to a rich diversity of communities, restaurants, and other cultural factors as a reason why they favor higher immigration levels. Such an argument would have a great deal of appeal to themselves, because of their orientation towards novel experiences. However, they may be focusing on points that are unproductive or counterproductive, if they are talking to a conservative who prefers the familiar and routine.

Take another example: Imagine a televised debate between a liberal and a conservative about police abuse in black communities and the proper level of oversight to minimize it. Liberals who favor stringent oversight and harsh penalties might base their arguments on their deeply felt belief in the importance of police treating all communities fairly, and showing care toward all communities. Structuring the argument this way would likely resonate with liberals in the audience, since the argument appeals directly to the moral foundations. But it might not have strong appeal to conservatives, since they care about other moral dimensions equally.

Imagine that instead of simply arguing the caring and fairness dimensions, the liberal might also suggest that more stringent rules further the authority of the police management over the rank and file officers, as well as strengthen the authority of the government over the police. Further, a liberal savvy to moral foundations theory might further argue that police abuse is a violation of the loyalty that police need to show to citizens. Such arguments, if executed with reasonable skill, provide additional resonance with conservative observers of the debate.

This workbook advocates that you not argue with racism skeptics, but rather engage in experience-sharing and mutual storytelling. Still, the orientation differences described above are relevant to how you might tell your Connect and Expand stories. Specifically, if you are a liberal ally trying to influence a conservative skeptic, consider tweaking your anecdotes to show that you have some fealty to other moral frameworks besides your own.

Suppose for instance, you are telling an anecdote about being pulled over by a police officer, and your primary takeaway from the anecdote is that you think you benefited from unearned racial advantage and positive assumptions because you are white. You might describe your attitude of compliance as the officer approached you as not fear and resentment of police authority, but rather respect and appreciation for their devotion to public service and the dangers they endure. If your car is a place you keep clean and orderly, you might add that small detail to your story.

The suggestion that you consider such tweaks to your anecdotes in this way is not meant to lead you to present yourself falsely. Your goal is to have an authentic encounter, and truth telling is key to authentic interactions. At the same time, if there is a mix of motivations or emotions in a situation, it might make sense to lift up elements that will connect you to the skeptic and their ideology and moral framework.

WHY ANTI-RACIST PROGRESSIVES NEED TO SUPPORT CONSERVATIVES

Earlier in this workbook, a claim was made that you undermine your efforts at transforming denial about racism if the skeptic thinks that you are trying to change their entire political worldview. This point merits some additional amplification.

Most allies have seen liberals who think that racism does not exist, since these people are not hard to find. However, many white allies have never met or even heard of someone who is politically conservative but willing to acknowledge unconscious racial bias and institutional racism exist and create racial inequities that merit attention. The primary reason that many allies have not heard of people like this, is the conservative movement has been purposely managed for decades to appeal to a white racial grievance. This grievance is at odds with the idea that racism against POC is a problem worthy of specific attention. A secondary reason that many liberal allies have not encountered anti-racist conservatives is because they have minimal exposure to conservatives in their real lives, on social media, or in mass media.

This almost total isolation from conservatives has a number of negative side effects on the mindset that liberal allies need to be effective. As discussed in Part One, many white allies – and liberals generally – often do not extend dignity to conservatives when they are interacting with them. Besides being a spiritual problem, denying people dignity undermines the comity that is useful in a diverse democracy. This tendency to regard conservative views as largely illegitimate is amplified in a "liberal media echo chamber" and, not surprisingly, produces a backlash resentment that gets amplified through a "conservative media echo chamber".

Partially because of this history of being denied basic dignity across the ideological divide, it is difficult for many conservatives to entertain the idea that racism against POC is real and hurts America. In addition to whatever dignity-denying direct experiences they might have had talking to liberals about race, the conservative echo chamber also primes many

> It will be valuable to envision that this person can recognize that reality of racism and still tend to prefer conservative approaches to solving society's problems.

to deny racism. While the idea that racism is real is not inherently a liberal idea, it has become associated with liberalism within the conservative media. For this reason also, conservatives come to the conversation already primed to dismiss racism's existence as just some other liberal talking point.

To counter the above, it is useful if you approach the skeptic from the perspective that you are not trying to change their entire political ideology or their entire orientation to life. It is best if you can operate from the motivation not to turn them into liberals like you are (if that is true). Rather, convey you are trying to get them to stop denying that racism against POC is real and that it has important moral implications for society.

To do this, it will be valuable to envision that this person can recognize that reality of racism and still prefer conservative approaches to solving society's problems. This will be difficult for many white allies, since they have little or no exposure to conservatives who could be reasonably described as anti-racist. Still, you will be most effective if you imagine that people like this exist.

This not to say that it is unimportant to advocate for liberal positions. Rather, the point is that when you are trying to influence a conservative to move out of denial about racism, there is a big downside to linking that to your general liberal views. It is highly likely that they will perceive conceding that racism is real as equivalent to making a concession about politics, and perhaps even about their worldview. Your goal is to not make the skeptic feel that their entire political ideology is being attacked. When talking with a racism skeptic (and perhaps only while it is happening) you should look at their degree of attraction to conservative policy solutions as a perspective to be welcomed into the mix of possible solutions.

Below are a few questions to reflect upon how ready you are to engage a conservative skeptic with the goal of diminishing their racism denial, but not to produce wholesale changes in their worldview.

How many people have you known personally, second-hand, or as public figures, who generally held conservative viewpoints but were, you thought, not in denial about the idea that racism against people of color was an actual problem?

I can think of ________ people who I might call anti-racist conservatives.

If you can remember their names, write them down.

____

____

____

____

____

How easy is it for you to imagine that a person could not be in denial/ resistance about racism but hold conservative views on other public/ political issues?

- Very hard to imagine
- Hard to imagine
- Takes a little work to imagine
- I can imagine this, though I have not seen it
- I have seen this once or twice, so I don't have to imagine it
- I have seen this many times and/or it is very easy to imagine this

Imagine that you have decided to engage a conservative racism skeptic in a series of discussions. Imagine that after a number of conversations, they have significantly moved out of their previous tendency to deny that unconscious bias is real, that institutional racism actually matters, and there is some moral obligation to address on-going inequities. At the same time, they still have conservative beliefs on a range of other issues, such as gun control, abortion, tax policy, immigration reform, and so on. How would you feel about the results of your hard work with them?

- Very disappointed that I have not gotten them to see the folly of their conservative views
- Appreciative of the movement, but this person still needs a lot more work from someone
- Pretty happy, but I have a gnawing sense that there is more I should do
- Very happy: I have done my job as an ally

If you notice that your answers to these questions suggest that is it difficult for you to envision an anti-racist conservatism, it might be useful to expose yourself to such people. Some white conservatives with a national profile who do not deny the existence of racism include analyst Max Boot, columnist Charlie Sykes, former presidential candidate Evan McMullen, and journalist Conor Friendsdorf.

CLOSING ENCOURAGEMENTS

Below are some closing thoughts meant to help allies stay on the important path that they are on.

SOME PERILS OF THE PATH OF THE ALLY

The past few years have seen a significant growth in the white ally arm of the anti-racism movement. Increasing numbers have become at least a little bit woke – or at least have adopted the associated language – and have tried to lend some support for various anti-oppression efforts led by POC. Overall, this has to be considered a good thing.

> White folks joining these existent racial equity movements creates myriad complexities - including new headaches - that must be managed by the people of color who are trying to lead the anti-racism movement.

Certainly, some of these new arrivals to the liberation movement are doing what some have called “performative wokeness”. They are putting on a show for themselves, their liberal white comrades, and perhaps some POC - to show they understand that racism is a problem. At the same time, other new arrivals bring energy to the anti-racism struggle, as these allies offer their best, but admittedly flawed, selves to the veterans of the anti-racism movement.

One thing that we have be honest about is the fact that white folks joining these existent racial equity movements create myriad complexities - including new headaches - that must be managed by the POC leaders. It’s great they want to join the crew, but new sailors need to be trained both in nautical tasks and in boat culture, and this requires more work on everyone's part. Training new crew members may make the captain's job more difficult and may even cause the boat to sail a little slower for a time.

It is unfortunate but not unreasonable that some organizers find this burden of working with novice white allies to be too much to bear, and thus sometimes subject white allies to high levels of scrutiny and sharp criticism. It is not difficult to find pointed critiques of white folks who get involved with POC anti-oppression movements. Often, these critiques describe how allies are participating poorly or doing so in a way that demonstrates they are still "coming from a place of privilege."[2] Even further, it is also not difficult to find well-written critiques that question the validity of white caucus spaces that aspire to work alongside of POC-led organizations.[3]

If white allies join existing anti-racism efforts, they will likely be criticized for how they do that. If they start their own organizations, they might be criticized for that as well. So what is a white ally supposed to do? Is there a way to avoid harsh criticism? Probably not.

White allies, especially those who deeply care about racism, occupy a liminal (i.e. in-between) space. On one side, POC activist comrades often see racism as the dominant factor of modern American life and have very stringent expectations—such as how allies should think about their role, how allies use language and concepts when discussing the work, and the right way to strike a balance between stepping forward and letting POC

2 https://theestablishment.co/welcome-to-the-anti-racism-movement-heres-what-you-ve-missed-711089cb7d34
https://medium.com/@lizdais_harding/white-allies-youre-likely-presenting-as-fake-woke-and-you-need-to-stop-b4890a1ddf0e
https://medium.com/athena-talks/for-other-white-people-who-want-to-stop-being-annoying-and-or-awful-allies-to-people-of-color-a-67d2d4015c75

3 https://www.huffingtonpost.com/entry/whites-only-surj-and-the-caucasian-invasion-of-racial_us_58dd5cf7e4b04ba4a5e25209

lead. On the other side are racism-skeptic cousins and friends who consider allies as liberal enablers of the sloth, dysfunction, and hypersensitivity of POC. Finally, there are white allies who think that harsh criticism of other allies is somehow useful to themselves and the movement.

Perhaps being a white ally – or any anti-racist advocate for that matter – means that you open yourself to criticism from many quarters. This is the path you are choosing.

In a time of increased racial tensions between white allies' comrades and their racism-skeptic cousins, it is not surprising they feel uncertain about what their role should be. In the face of these complex pressures, it is not surprising that many people who might be allies at the heart level do very little to move the equity ball forward. It is easy for good-hearted white folks to decide that active allyship is just too difficult. Apparently, you have chosen the ally path, since you have acquired this workbook. The hope of this project is that you stay on the path despite these pressures.

Perhaps some double binds are inevitable for anyone who is committed to disrupting unfairness that is deeply embedded in society's systems, when they have benefited from that same unfairness. Perhaps being a white ally – or any anti-racist advocate for that matter - means that you open yourself to criticism from many quarters. This is the path you are choosing.

This project is sympathetic to these crosscutting pressures. Its aim is to encourage and empower white allies, under the presumption that doing so will make it easier to take risks in their interactions with cousins, neighbors, and so on. The intention is to lovingly apply some strong nudges and guidance on conversations that white folks need to have with each other. The primary motivation behind this project is to make progress on racial equity in the U.S. But, it is worth noting that there are even bigger issues that depend on large numbers of white allies engaging skeptics.

UNPROCESSED WHITE GRIEVANCE IS UNDERMINING LEGITIMATE DEBATE ABOUT THE GLOBAL WORLD ORDER

One of the most pressing examples is an overdue conversation about the racial threat and the sense of grievance growing in America and many historically white countries. As was made clear in 2016, this unprocessed white grievance – often expressed as racism, xenophobia, and/or nativism - is having global geopolitical consequences. The entire world order is subject to being altered. White folks across the northern hemisphere are not talking to each other honestly about how they feel dislocated by the increased prominence demands of non-whites all over the world. There is a strong case to be made that the 2016 presidential election (and perhaps Brexit as well) was a massive failure by the white ally community.

Donald Trump's tendency to make racially-problematic statements and to stoke white grievance was well known and widely discussed in the mass media before the election. Those who think of themselves as anti-racist allies must ask themselves: how many risks did you take to have conversations about candidate Trump? And if you had these conversations with people who looked at him differently, how effective were you? Not necessarily in changing votes, but in getting people to honestly consider his stance on racial issues as a factor in their vote?

Certainly, there are reasons to oppose globalism and the inequities associated with it. The U.S. and other Western nations need to have debates on the advantages and disadvantages of the corporatist global order that has been in place for decades. But this debate needs to be an honest one, and not overly influenced by an historically uninformed and xenophobic sense of grievance by white populations. It is this conversation that white allies are in the best position to start. When POC raise this psychological undercurrent, the responses from racism skeptics tend toward denial, rage, and accusations of hypersensitivity and playing the so-called race card. And, POC are not commonly with white people in those private settings of potential emotional vulnerability. That is why exploring white grievance in private conversations is allies' work.

WHITE ALLIES CAN HELP WITH A CRITICAL NATIONAL WEAKNESS EVEN BIGGER THAN RACIAL INEQUITY

The work of white allies– if it involves the practices of dialogue and non-violent communication discussed herein - is important for an additional reason. This work is about recasting some very unfortunate cultural norms that are turning out to be weaknesses in American society.

Americans have become less able to talk to each other about important collective issues. The divisions between people of different political ideologies have grown in recent years, and our capacity to engage across lines of ideology seems to have severely eroded.

Even though commentators have been lamenting the decreased cooperation and sense of comity in our political culture for at least two decades, this issue seems to have worsened recently.

Increasingly, people who are anywhere except at the center of the ideological spectrum see people on the other side as threats to the nation.[4] This incapacity to presume the good will of others makes Two-thirds (66%) of consistently conservative Republicans see the Democratic Party as a threat to the nation's well-being, compared with the half (50%) of consistently liberal progress on pressing problems much more difficult. We know that this weakness has been exploited by those seeking to undermine the U.S.'s well-being. We can see this from the way that Russian operatives attacked the American polity in the 2016 election. They continue to use fake identities and robots on social media to inflame existing divisions between demographically and ideologically disparate groups.

As desperately as the nation needs a more activated white ally population to energize the movement for racial equity, the work can be looked at in light of a broader patriotic purpose – re- equipping Americans with the capacity to talk across ideological divides.

---

4 Two-thirds (66%) of consistently conservative Republicans see the Democratic Party as a threat to the nation's well-being, compared with the half (50%) of consistently liberal Democrats who say the same about the Republican Party. Among all Democrats and Democratic leaners, 27% go so far as to say the GOP is a threat to the well-being of the country. Among all Republicans and Republican leaners, more than a third (36%) say Democratic policies threaten the nation. From: Pew Research Center – 2014 Political Polarization in the American Public.

THE ALLY PATH, IF PURSUED BY TAKING RISKS, COULD BE CONSIDERED A NOBLE ONE

Raising uncomfortable issues of white racial grievance – and doing so consistently and with savvy and technique – requires taking risks. Even if you implement the storytelling-based tactics in this workbook with great skill, you may still become "that person who you have to be careful what you say around." You will be breaking the silence of the white folks in your circle of influence, by raising issues of white grievance, bias, and historical racism.

For example, some costs that societal racism imposes upon whites include "No Go" areas in the urban core, excessive suburbanization, the maintenance of a massive private school system (to make up for the deficits of neglected public school systems), and an insufficient sense of community with spiritual dimensions. This is but a partial list. Allies need to think through this for themselves and talk with other white folks, skeptics and allies alike. In fact, discourse about "How does racism harm whites?" is an underdeveloped theme within the white ally community. Your considered thoughts and tactics for discussing this need to be part of your toolkit, too.

Nevertheless, as real as these prices are for white folks, they still get a net benefit from the racial hierarchies that are the status quo in America. The ally path is one that involves spending energy trying to bring down an unfair system that ultimately brings the ally more payoffs. This is why the walk of the ally – stumbles notwithstanding – is a noble one for those who are truly on it.

The path of the ally is arguably a noble one because allies are consciously taking social risks by ending the silence about race in white settings that are ideologically mixed. It is noble because being effective requires taking risks and troubling the waters. It is noble because this path is about truly engaging people over the most intractable issue in American history, and is not in the ally's direct self-interest to do this.

HUMILITY AND A SPIRIT OF INQUIRY WILL BE IMPORTANT

If you tell comrades in the anti-racism movement that you practice the methods herein, you will be told they are weak-willed, lacking backbone, too slow, or problematic in some other way. Others claim that these methods will not work. You must be prepared for this reaction. To put it bluntly, you will be criticized – including by POC who may be leaders of anti-racism efforts you participate in. And given the inherent questions and doubts that POC have toward allies - and the need for your allyship to sometimes involve working with them - your humility in the face of the criticism is important.

> You will be told by many that these approaches are weak-willed, lacking backbone, not getting the urgency of the racial equity problem, or problematic in some other way... You must be prepared for this reaction.

Fortunately, one can be humble and still stand your ground about your belief that you should engage in empathetic listening strategies with other white people. As has been discussed, there is good social science research behind the notion that empathetic listening strategies are more effect in persuasion. More pointedly, you should look at your own actual experience, and be willing to talk about it. As recommended in the reflection exercise at the start of this section, you should interrogate your interpersonal influence to find what your life has actually taught you. Based on your own experience and that of science, you should push back against such critiques of these methods, and do so in the spirit of helping others improve their practice of influencing people.

At the same time, the spirit of dialogue and inquiry embodied in the approach of this project suggests that you should not be overly doctrinaire about what has been presented herein. Maybe the folks who advocate more combative approaches are right, or at least right in some circumstances. Everyone in the racial equity movement should be open-minded about what persuasion strategies work, since no one really knows. There have not been large-scale experiments involving hundreds or thousands of people awakening others from their denial about racism.

So, if someone truly believes that more combative and/or prophetic approaches work, and if they really want to challenge the methods here, perhaps the answer is to conduct your own small-scale experiments. If someone is serious about effectiveness in changing people's thinking about racism, and not just sniping at you for not being "woke enough", perhaps the best strategy is to pretend both of you have a research grant to compare approaches. Try coming to some agreement about how they differ, how to define a reasonable attempt to influence someone, and what success looks like. It would be great if each of you got others to participate, so you have more data to look at.

As noted, this project is based on specific goal - reducing the proportion (55%) of whites who think racism against POC is not a specific problem requiring attention. As important as is the goal of reducing this proportion to 45% by 2025, it is overshadowed by something bigger. A critical national question concerns whether a democracy based on the exchange of ideas can actually survive the many forces causing silo-ization, a decline of civility, and a diminished public square. Another crucial national question is whether the U.S. wants to retreat from the corporatist global order it has built since World War II. It may be that that the widespread deployment of principles from persuasion science, conflict resolution, and non-violent communication can actually help tens of millions of white Americans get past their blind spots. If this turns out to be true, there hope for future conversations among members of this increasingly diverse nation about the race issues that threaten it. Moreover, there is hope for other challenges that now go unaddressed because of the ideological divides.

Thank you for your passion and, most importantly, your ongoing efforts that, while potentially flawed and subject to numerous missteps, are also noble and even patriotic.

ADDITIONAL RESOURCES

Some resources that allies might use to bolster their understanding of key topics in this workbook.

ADDITIONAL RESOURCES

OTHERING

ARTICLES AVAILABLE ONLINE

- Brons, Lajos. (2015). Othering, An Analysis. Transcience, a Journal of Global Studies. 6. 69-90. https://www2.hu-berlin.de/transcience/Vol6_No1_2015_69_90.pdf
- The Problem of Othering: Towards Inclusiveness and Belonging. John A. Powell and Stephen Menendian, JUN 29, 2016, Othering &Belonging: Expanding the Circle of Human Concern, http://www.otheringandbelonging.org/the-problem-of-othering/
- The Use of Othering in the Formation of a Nationalist Society. John Evans. http://www.academia.edu/1338990/The_Use_of_Othering_in_the_Formation_of_a_Nationalist_Society

SHORT EXPLANATORY VIDEOS

- *othering: Who is "Different"? Margaret McCune. https://youtu.be/OrBqj2M_Sqc*
- *Professor John Powell Talks About The Language Of 'Othering' During The 2016 Election - Part 1. CBS. https://youtu.be/zBwme7v9QM8*
- *The othering of ethnic minorities. Hannah Armstrong. https://youtu.be/LKeDwMU0_Jo*

UNCONSCIOUS BIAS

ARTICLES AVAILABLE ONLINE

- Journal of Experimental Social Psychology. Volume 48, Issue 6, November 2012, Pages 1267-1278. *Long-term reduction in implicit race bias: A prejudice habit-breaking intervention.* Patricia G. Devine, Patrick S. Forscher, Anthony J. Austin, William T. L. Cox. https://www.ncbi.nlm.nih.gov/pmc/articles/PMC3603687/
- *Understanding Unconscious Bias and Unintentional Racism.* Jean Moule. Phi Delta Kappan, v90 n5 p320-326 Jan 2009. http://people.uncw.edu/browna/documents/UnderstandingUnconsciousBiasUnintentionalRacism.pdf

- Minikel-Lacocque, J. (2012). *Racism, College, and the Power of Words: Racial Microaggressions Reconsidered.* American Educational Research Journal. https://www.uww.edu/Documents/diversity/racism.pdf

SHORT EXPLANATORY VIDEOS

- *Understanding Unconscious Bias.* The Royal Society. https://youtu.be/dVp9Z5k0dEE
- *Unconscious Bias @ Work — Making the Unconscious Conscious.* Life at Google. https://youtu.be/NW5s_-Nl3JE
- *What is Unconscious Bias?* Employers network for equality and inclusion. https://youtu.be/rbe5D3Yh43o

ATTRIBUTION ERROR

ARTICLES AVAILABLE ONLINE

- *Fundamental Attribution Error.* Wikipedia, the free encyclopedia. https://en.wikipedia.org/wiki/Fundamental_attribution_error
- *The Fundamental Attribution Error.* PsychWiki - A Collaborative Psychology Wiki. https://www.saylor.org/site/wp-content/uploads/2010/12/The-Fundamental-Attribution-Error.pdf
- *Explanations and Implications of The Fundamental Attribution Error: A Review and Proposal.* Zachariah Berry. Journal of Integrated Social Sciences. http://jiss.org/documents/volume_5/issue_1/JISS%202015%205(1)%2044-57%20FAE.pdf

SHORT EXPLANATORY VIDEOS

- *Attribution theory - Attribution error and culture.* Khan Academy. https://youtu.be/XYWFGJ2aYRU
- *Fundamental Attribution Error: Definition & Overview.* Social Psychology: Tutoring Solution. http://study.com/academy/lesson/fundamental-attribution-error-definition-lesson-quiz.html#courseInfo
- *Ethics Defined: Fundamental Attribution Error.* UT McCombs School of Business. https://youtu.be/k0HUujS88jQ

ADDITIONAL RESOURCES

RACIAL ANXIETY

ARTICLES AVAILABLE ONLINE

- *Racial Anxiety*. Perception Institute. https://perception.org/research/racial-anxiety/
- Godsil, Rachel D. and Richardson, L. Song, *Racial Anxiety* (August 15, 2017). Iowa Law Review, Vol. 102, No. 5, 2017, Forthcoming; UC Irvine School of Law Research Paper No. 2017-40. Available at SSRN: https://ssrn.com/abstract=3019388
- *Two new studies find racial anxiety is the biggest driver of support for Trump*. By Christopher Ingraham. June 6, 2016. The Washington Post. https://www.washingtonpost.com/news/wonk/wp/2016/06/06/racial-anxiety-is-a-huge-driver-of-support-for-donald-trump-two-new-studies-find/

SHORT EXPLANATORY VIDEOS

- *Defining Implicit Bias and Racial Anxiety*. National Association of Independent Schools (NAIS) https://youtu.be/msscegmQpW0?t=45
- *Do White People Get Stressed Talking About Race?* Buzzfeed. https://youtu.be/YX-i11IGj5w
- *Is disarming 'racial anxiety' the key to moving forward?* MSNBC. http://www.msnbc.com/the-cycle/watch/is-disarming-racial-anxiety-the-key-to-moving-forward-45218883944

UNEARNED RACIAL ADVANTAGE (COMMONLY CALLED WHITE PRIVILEGE)

ARTICLES AVAILABLE ONLINE

- *On Racism and White Privilege*. Teaching Tolerance. https://www.tolerance.org/professional-development/on-racism-and-white-privilege
- *White Privilege: Unpacking the Invisible Knapsack*. Peace and Freedom Magazine, July/August, 1989, pp. 10-12. https://nationalseedproject.org/white-privilege-unpacking-the-invisible-knapsack

- *Understanding White Privilege.* Francis E. Kendall, Ph.D. 2002. https://www.cpt.org/files/Undoing%20Racism%20-%20 Understanding%20White%20Privilege%20-%20Kendall.pdf

SHORT EXPLANATORY VIDEOS

- *White Privilege Explained.* The Young Turks. https://youtu. be/19Cb4DOnIF4
- *Not All White People Were Created Equal: White Privilege in America.* Fusion. https://youtu.be/ZN9mwhSrTdU
- *White Privilege.* Sociology Live! https://youtu.be/ZLgbw_A1mLI

RACIAL THREAT

- *Racial Threat.* Wikipedia. https://en.wikipedia.org/wiki/Racial_threat
- Cindy Brooks Dollar, *Racial Threat Theory: Assessing the Evidence, Requesting Redesign.* Journal of Criminology, vol. 2014, Article ID 983026, 7 pages, 2014. doi:10.1155/2014/983026. https://www.hindawi. com/archive/2014/983026/
- Stephan, Walter & Cookie, W.S.. (2000). *An Integrated Threat Theory of Prejudice."* In Stuart Oskamp (ed.). Reducing Prejudice and Discrimination. 23-46. https://books.google.com/ books?hl=en&lr=&id=aOyFEy-yzMoC&oi=fnd&pg=PA23&dq=racial+t hreat+theory&ots=oKMH8UoDxL&sig=b6pgxTWkuIoRk1gp0yewGFxI mrs#v=onepage&q=racial%20threat%20theory&f=false

WHITE BACKLASH

ARTICLES AVAILABLE ONLINE

- *Analysis of the 'White Backlash'.* William Lee Miller. Aug. 23, 1964. The New York Times. http://www.nytimes.com/1964/08/23/analysis-of-the-white-backlash.html
- *Will Immigration Spark a White Backlash in America?* Marisa Abrajano. Issues in Governance Studies. Number 67. July 2014. https://www.brookings.edu/wp-content/uploads/2016/06/Abrajano_ Immigration_v03.pdf

- *Belonging, racism and white backlash in the 2016 US Presidential Election*. Dr Deborah Gabriel. US Election Analysis 2016: Media, Voters and the Campaign. http://www.academia.edu/29975054/Belonging_racism_and_white_backlash_in_the_2016_US_Presidential_Election

SHORT EXPLANATORY VIDEOS

- *MLK discusses "The White Backlash" 1967*. https://youtu.be/vWKri1HEVRg
- *White Backlash Against Progress: The 3rd Reconstruction*. Story of America. https://youtu.be/Zoo3GEfhPwo
- *Just Like After Reconstruction, Trump Vote Highlights White Backlash to Recent Racial Progress. Democracy Now. https://youtu.be/lWMCjTkokrQ*

INSTITUTIONAL RACISM VS STRUCTURAL RACISM

- *Glossary for Understanding the Dismantling Structural Racism/Promoting Racial Equity Analysis*. The Aspen Institute. https://assets.aspeninstitute.org/content/uploads/files/content/docs/rcc/RCC-Structural-Racism-Glossary.pdf
- *Discrimination Comes in Many Forms: Individual, Institutional, and Structural*. Fred L. Pincus. Readings for Diversity and Social Justice. Edited by Maurianne Adams, etc., Published 2000. http://media.lanecc.edu/users/martinezp/250%20CRG/Discrim.pdf

RACIAL INEQUITY

ARTICLES AVAILABLE ONLINE

- *What Is Racial Equity?* Center for Social Inclusion. http://www.centerforsocialinclusion.org/our-work/what-is-racial-equity/
- *Understanding the System of Racial Inequity*. Racial Equity Tools. https://www.racialequitytools.org/module/understanding-the-system-of-racial-inequity

- *Racial Inequity and How to Dismantle It.* YWCA. http://www.wche.org/uploads/8/8/9/8/8898682/racial_inequity_and_how_to_dismantle_it.pdf

SHORT EXPLANATORY VIDEOS

- *"Micro- inequity" Defined.* Jeanne Martinson. https://youtu.be/WeZ9C56PfC8
- *The Unequal Opportunity Race.* The African American Policy Forum. https://youtu.be/vX_Vzl-r8NY
- *Issues Facing Us on Racial Inequity.* Net Impact. https://youtu.be/UplNdXjBKys

Made in the USA
Columbia, SC
24 April 2019